目 录 CONTENTS

第一单元　介绍和推荐　Unit One Introduction and Recommendation

第二单元　城市与环境　Unit Two City and Environment

第三单元　家居与购物　Unit Three Home and Shopping

第四单元　学校生活　*Unit Four School Life*

第五单元　健康　*Unit Five Health*

第六单元　娱乐与休闲　*Unit Six Entertainment and Leisure*

第七单元 新闻与传媒 *Unit Seven News and Media*

第八单元 旅行与习俗 *Unit Eight Travel and Custom*

附录

Unit One Introduction and Recommendation
第一单元 介绍和推荐

第一课 我从北京来

1. Write the tones of the words or phrases, then translate them.

xingming	guoji	riqi	zhiye	dianhua	jieshao
姓名	国籍	日期	职业	电话	介绍
chusheng	didian	zhuzhi	xingbie	youjian	ziji
出生	地点	住址	性别	邮件	自己

2. Write the characters.

笔画数						
	cóng					
	xìng					
	chū					

	qī					
	zhù					
	yóu					

3. Make new words or phrases based on the characters given.

生 shēng	籍 jí	住 zhù	点 diǎn
性 xìng	日 rì	姓 xìng	期 qī
址 zhǐ	别 bié	业 yè	出 chū
名 míng	职 zhí	地 dì	国 guó

1) ________ 2) ________ 3) ________ 4) ________

5) ________ 6) ________ 7) ________ 8) ________

4. Write characters using the following example radicals.

亻 你 ________________

讠 话 ________________

土 地 ________________

女 妈 ________________

5. Fill in the blanks with the given words following the text.

五　运动　电视　十五　有名　音乐

1) 王明明今年______岁，他是北京人，他家有______个人。他喜欢看______和听______，也喜欢______。他说北京的故宫和长城很______。

香港　丽丽　上海　小红

2) 丽丽今年十四岁，______比______大一点儿。丽丽家在______，小红家在______。

6. Complete the sentences following the examples.

1)

我	从	北京	来	。
你		哪儿		？
				。

2)

欢迎	你	来	北京	。
	你	来		。
				。

7. Make sentences to describe the pictures by rearranging the words.

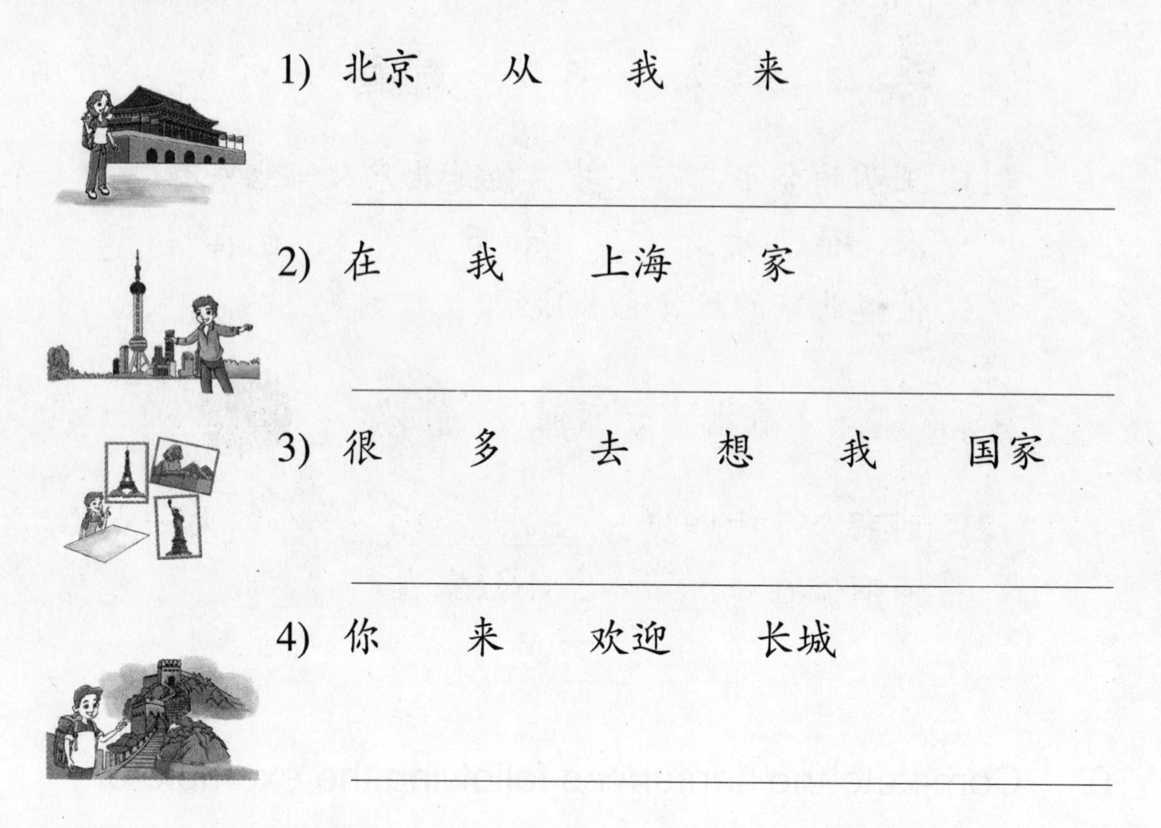

1) 北京　从　我　来

____

2) 在　我　上海　家

____

3) 很　多　去　想　我　国家

____

4) 你　来　欢迎　长城

____

8. Answer the following questions according to Exercise 4 of the Student's Book.

1) "我"是谁?

____

2) "我"的住址在哪儿?

____

3) "我"的生日是几月几号?

____

4) "我"的中国朋友从哪儿来?

____

5) "我"的中国朋友是女孩子吗?

____

9. Fill in the form with your own information.

姓　　名		性　　别		国　　籍	
出生日期			出生地点		
职　　业			电　　话		
住　　址					
电子邮箱					

10. Make a business card for yourself in Chinese.

11. Draw a picture of your family or your friends and write down their personal information such as occupations, nationalities, etc.

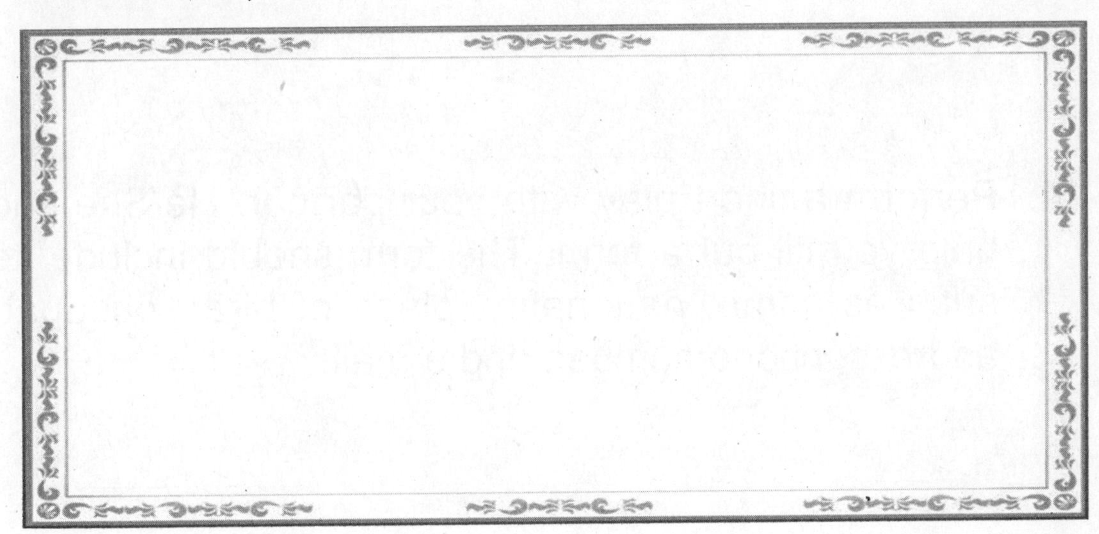

12. Fill in the blanks with the correct characters and write a similar paragraph of your own.

我_________丽丽，他_________明明，我今年十四_________，我_________明明小一岁。我_________北京来，明明家_________上海。

____

____

____

13. Listen and answer the following questions.

1) Mike是哪国人？

____

2) 故宫和长城在哪儿？

____

3) “我”的新朋友是男孩子还是女孩子？

____

4) “我们”一起说什么语？为什么？

____

14. Perform a short play with your partner. He/She should help you fill out a form. The form should include items such as name, nationality, place of birth, occupation, address, phone number, and e-mail.

15. Practice writing more characters.

笔画数						

第二课　我想来兼职

1. Write the tones of the words or phrases, then translate them.

waiyu	keshi	shenqing	shengyi	nüshi	zuo	jingyan
外语	可是	申请	生意	女士	做	经验
suiran	xunlian	jianzhi	chule	yiwai	jin	mianshi
虽然	训练	兼职	除了	以外	进	面试

2. Write the characters.

笔画数						
	wài					
	yǔ					
	liàn					

	qǐng					
	kě					
	shì					

3. Make new words or phrases based on the characters given.

生 shēng	是 shì	意 yì	外 wài
练 liàn	女 nǚ	请 qǐng	虽 suī
可 kě	语 yǔ	职 zhí	然 rán
申 shēn	士 shì	兼 jiān	训 xùn

1) ________ 2) ________ 3) ________ 4) ________

5) ________ 6) ________ 7) ________ 8) ________

4. Write characters using the following example radicals.

讠 请 ____________________

辶 这 ____________________

5. Fill in the blanks with the given words following the text.

上课　休息　运动　电脑

1) 虽然今年暑假我没有________，可是我很高兴。我在一个学校学习________和英语，有很多新朋友，我们除了________，还一起________和看电影。

会　能　想

2) 你好，王经理，我________来兼职。我________说英语和法语。虽然我没做过生意，可是我在商店做过售货员，我有一点儿工作经验，我________试试吗？

6. Complete the sentences following the examples.

1)

除了	英语	以外	，	我还会	法语	。
除了		以外	，	我还会		。
			，			。

2)

课	虽然	难	，	可是	很有意思	。
公园		小	，		很漂亮	。
			，			。

3)

你	说	得	很好	。
他	学	得		。
				。

4)

我	在	商店	做	过	售货员	。
哥哥		北京	去		长城	。
						。

7. Make sentences to describe the pictures by rearranging the words.

1) 我　喜欢　除了　游泳　还　以外　足球

____

2) 卧室　虽然　舒服　可是　小　很

____

3) 她　不　好　很　得　打

____

4) 他　表演　在　过　太极拳　运动场

____

5) 他　学习　想　书法　来

____

8. Decide True (T) or False (F) according to Exercise 4 of the Student's Book.

1) 今天“我”有汉语课和体育课，课不多。(　　)
2) “我”不会做中国菜，可是我想学。(　　)
3) 爸爸在一个学校的医院工作。(　　)
4) “我”想吃这个东西。(　　)

9. Tell us what type of job you would like to have.

____

____

____

10. Fill in the blanks with the correct characters and write a similar paragraph of your own.

昨天我________了一个朋友的家。在他的家我们一起________了一个中国电影。虽然我________过那个电影，可是我很喜欢。我们除了________电影以外，还一起________了音乐。

____

____

____

11. Listen and answer the following questions.

1) “我”去过什么地方？

____

2) “我”说什么地方最好？

____

3) “我”和爸爸、妈妈做了什么？

____

4) 今年夏天“我”去哪儿？

____

12. Role play: Pretend you want to apply for a job and your partner needs to give you an interview. Please introduce yourself and talk about your education background, work experience, and talents.

13. Practice writing more characters.

笔画数						

Additional Vocabulary

轮滑	lúnhuá	skating
滑板	huábǎn	skateboard
跳舞	tiàowǔ	to dance
演奏	yǎnzòu	to play a musical instrument
乐器	yuèqì	musical instrument
俱乐部	jùlèbù	club

第三课　我们给他打电话吧

1. Write the tones of the words or phrases, then translate them.

mingpian	keyi	waimai	song	caidan	zhang
名片	可以	外卖	送	菜单	张
kuaican	yangrou	e	ti	zhuanqian	gei
快餐	羊肉	饿	替	赚钱	给

2. Write the characters.

笔画数						
	tì					
	mài					
	è					

	gěi					
	piàn					
	yáng					

3. Make new words or phrases based on the characters given.

以 yǐ	名 míng	单 dān	快 kuài
片 piàn	职 zhí	羊 yáng	赚 zhuàn
餐 cān	外 wài	钱 qián	菜 cài
卖 mài	肉 ròu	兼 jiān	可 kě

1) ________ 2) ________ 3) ________ 4) ________

5) ________ 6) ________ 7) ________ 8) ________

4. Write characters with the following example radicals.

饣 饭 ________________________

辶 近 ________________________

5. Fill in the blanks with the given words following the text.

说　试试　来　工作　做

1) 我的朋友想______学校的图书馆兼职，他会______英语和法语，也______过图书馆的兼职，他很喜欢在图书馆______。他可以来______吗？

吃　打　送　饿　点

2) 现在我们______了，可是我们不想做饭，想______快餐。我们给一个朋友______电话，他替附近的一个饭馆______外卖，我们想______那个饭馆的烤羊肉。

6. Complete the sentences following the examples.

1)

这	个	房间	是	我	的	。
这		衣服	是		的	。
						。

2)

他	替	朋友	订	票	。
	替		准备		。
					。

3)

我	给	弟弟	买	书	。
	给				。
					。

7. Make sentences to describe the pictures by rearranging the words.

1) 我们　是　那个　的　教室

____

2) 妈妈　妹妹　衣服　替　穿

____

3) 给　老师　上　学生　课

____

4) 饿　我　很　的　肚子

____

5) 那个　有　学校　电话　我　的

____

8. Answer the following questions according to Exercise 4 of the Student's Book.

1) “我”的朋友从哪儿来?

____

2) “我”不喜欢打网球吗?

____

3) 这个房间是谁的? 旁边的大房间是谁的?

____

4) “我”常常跟妹妹一起做什么?

____

9. Talk about which fast food restaurants you eat at most often, where they are, and what your favourite fast food is.

____

____

____

10. Fill in the blanks with the correct characters and write a similar paragraph of your own.

我有一个朋友，他________美国来。昨天我________他打了电话，问（wèn, to ask）他可以替我________DVD吗，因为我很喜欢美国的电影。他说他去给我________。

____

____

____

11. Listen and answer the following questions.

1) Mary今天怎么了？

____

2) 她现在怎么样？

____

3) 医生说什么？

____

4) “我”给她准备了什么？

____

12. Role play: Pretend you are looking for a restaurant for lunch. Your partner recommends a restaurant to you. Discuss information including dishes, price, address, and services (such as take-out).

13. Practice writing more characters.

笔画数						

Additional Vocabulary

发	fā	to send
留言	liúyán	to leave word
短信	duǎnxìn	short message
写	xiě	to write

第四课 北京有一个很大的广场

1. Write the tones of the words or phrases, then translate them.

zhongxin	chengshi	guangchang	fengzheng	zhanlan	fang
中心	城市	广场	风筝	展览	放
bowuguan	qichezhan	huochezhan	jichang	ditie	ting
博物馆	汽车站	火车站	机场	地铁	停

2. Write the characters.

笔画数	
	bó
	chǎng
	shì

	zhǎn					
	lǎn					
	fàng					

3. Make new words or phrases based on the characters given.

广 guǎng	博 bó	铁 tiě	站 zhàn
览 lǎn	车 chē	停 tíng	车 chē
地 dì	物 wù	城 chéng	汽 qì
馆 guǎn	车 chē	火 huǒ	市 shì
场 chǎng	展 zhǎn	站 zhàn	场 chǎng

1) ________ 2) ________ 3) ________

4) ________ 5) ________ 6) ________

7) ________ 8) ________ 9) ________

4. Write characters using the following radicals.

土 ________________

宀 ________________

5. Fill in the blanks with the given words following the text.

东边　北边　市中心

1) 天安门广场在北京______，中国国家博物馆在天安门广场的______，故宫在天安门广场的______。

没有　很　过　那么

2) 我去过北京。北京______大，我们的城市______北京______大。北京有很多博物馆，我去______中国国家博物馆。

6. Complete the sentences following the examples.

1)

那个饭馆	有	很	好吃	的	鱼	。
			舒服		房间	。
						。

2)

今天	没有	昨天	那么	冷	。
	没有		那么		。
					。

3)

我	有	二十	多	块	钱	。
这个医院	有				医生	。
						。

7. Make sentences to describe the pictures by rearranging the words.

1) 一个　大　有　很　花园　市中心　的

____

2) 米饭　面条　好吃　没有

____

3) 多　我　朋友　个　有　三十

____

4) 很　考试　难　汉语

____

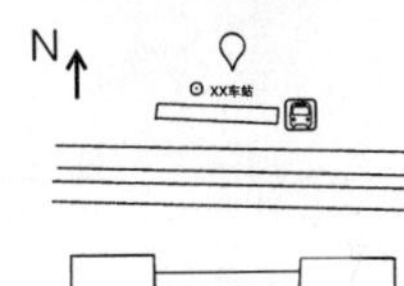

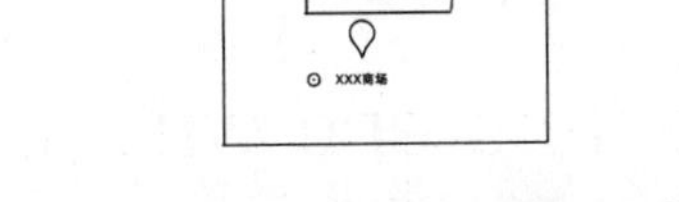

5) 在　的　商店　北边　汽车站

____

8. Answer the following questions according to Exercise 4 of the Student's Book.

1) "我"和爷爷去哪儿?

____

2) 北京和香港，哪个地方热?

____

3) 今天的作业怎么样? 难吗?

____

4) "我"喜欢学校的图书馆吗?

____

5) 在天安门广场的东边是什么？

____

9. Draw a map of Tian'anmen Square based on the description in the text and describe places of interest.

10. Fill in the blanks with the correct characters and write a similar paragraph of your own.

这______市中心的火车站，这个火车站很大，人很多。商店______火车站的南边。火车站______二十多个小商店，你来火车站的时候可以买东西，吃快餐，休息。这有一个很大的停车场，入口______左边，出口______右边。

____

____

____

11. Listen and answer the following questions.

1) 春天的时候有什么节日？可以做什么？

____

2) 秋天的时候有什么节日？可以做什么？

____

3) 中国什么地方有海滩？

____

4) “我”出生的城市有多少个学校？可以在学校学汉语吗？

____

5) 北京的冬天冷吗？香港的冬天呢？

____

12. Role play: Pretend you're going to bring some food to sell. Discuss with your partner where and why to sell it: for example, beside a car park, in a square, etc.

13. Practice writing more characters.

笔画数						

Additional Vocabulary

这儿	zhèr	here
那儿	nàr	there
西边	xībian	west
上边	shàngbian	on
下边	xiàbian	under
银行	yínháng	bank
超市	chāoshì	supermarket
餐厅	cāntīng	dining room
咖啡馆	kāfēiguǎn	café

第五课　郊区没有污染

1. Write the tones of the words or phrases, then translate them.

shumu	lü(se)	anquan	kongqi	cao	lu
树木	绿（色）	安全	空气	草	路
waibian	jiaoqu	gonggong qiche	wuran	li	niao
外边	郊区	公共汽车	污染	离	鸟

2. Write the characters.

笔画数						
	jiāo					
	qū					
	shù					

	mù					
	ān					
	quán					

3. Make new words or phrases based on the characters given.

木 mù	车 chē	区 qū	风 fēng
郊 jiāo	气 qì	污 wū	空 kōng
绿 lǜ	共 gòng	染 rǎn	舒 shū
景 jǐng	公 gōng	服 fú	汽 qì
全 quán	安 ān	色 sè	树 shù

1) ______________ 2) ______________ 3) ______________

4) ______________ 5) ______________ 6) ______________

7) ______________ 8) ______________ 9) ______________

4. Write characters using the following radicals.

木 ______________________________

氵 ______________________________

5. Fill in the blanks with the given words following the text.

开　坐　离

1) 我家______市中心很远，爸爸每天______车去工作，我______公共汽车去上课。可是我喜欢我家外边的风景，因为没有污染。

还　近　远　除了

2) 我家不在市中心，在城市外边，离市中心很______，可是汽车站离我家很______。我喜欢郊区，______风景漂亮，______没有污染。

6. Complete the sentences following the examples.

1)

今天的新闻	有意思	极了	。
	舒服		。
			。

2)

那个电影	好	得	不得了	。
	贵			。
				。

3)

饭馆	离	公园	很近	。
地铁		学校	远吗	?
			不远	。
				。

7. Make sentences to describe the pictures by rearranging the words.

1) 我 有 很 的 多 家 树木 旁边

____

2) 不 里 好 的 空气 房间

____

3) 离 远 商店 不 汽车站

____

4) 热 不得了 夏天 得

____

5) 饿 我 极了 现在

____

8. Decide True (T) or False (F) according to Exercise 4 of the Student's Book.

1) “我”家离长城不太远。(　　)
2) 今年春天北京很干净，因为常常下雨。(　　)
3) “我”喜欢小明家的花园，因为花很多。(　　)
4) “我”早上七点去学校，因为“我”喜欢学校。(　　)
5) 朋友的家在郊区，很安全，也很漂亮，可是不舒服。
(　　)

9. What are the advantages and disadvantages of living in an urban or rural area? Draw pictures and talk about your opinions in Chinese.

10. Fill in the blanks with the correct characters and write a similar paragraph of your own.

我家在郊区的一个湖______，湖里有很多船，风景很漂亮，我最喜欢有雪的时候。我家前边有一个不大的______，可是花很多，常常有很多小鸟来唱歌，妈妈很喜欢这个花园。我家后边有一个很小的运动场，我常常______朋友一起打篮球。

____

____

____

____

11. Listen and answer the following questions.

1) “我”什么时候去了长城？长城在哪儿？

____

2) 爸爸每天送“我”去学校吗？

____

3) 花园里有什么？

____

4) “我”想去哪儿？

____

12. Discussion: Talk with your partner about the advantages and disadvantages of living in the city or suburbs. Discuss shopping, entertainment, schools, sports, transportation, pollution, price, and housing.

13. Practice writing more characters.

笔画数						

Additional Vocabulary

爬山	pá shān	mountain climbing
钓鱼	diào yú	fishing
划船	huá chuán	boating
跑步	pǎobù	run
烧烤	shāokǎo	barbecue

第六课　我是本地人

1. Write the tones of the words or phrases, then translate them.

diqu	jingcha ju	shiye	tielu	zhao	renxingdao	mianfei
地区	警察局	失业	铁路	找	人行道	免费
youju	tudi	gonglu	cesuo	shiwu	jiedao	zhongjian
邮局	土地	公路	厕所	失物	街道	中间

2. Write the characters.

笔画数					
	jiē				
	dào				
	gōng				

	lù					
	běn					
	tǔ					

3. Make new words or phrases based on the characters given.

区 qū	街 jiē	所 suǒ	局 jú
业 yè	本 běn	察 chá	人 rén
地 dì	警 jǐng	铁 tiě	厕 cè
公 gōng	道 dào	地 dì	道 dào
行 xíng	路 lù	路 lù	失 shī

1) ______________ 2) ______________ 3) ______________

4) ______________ 5) ______________ 6) ______________

7) ______________ 8) ______________ 9) ______________

4. Write characters using the following radicals.

彳 ______________________________

⻊ ______________________________

5. Fill in the blanks with the given words following the text.

铁路　本地　土地　公路

1) 我是________人，我家在________旁边，离火车站很近。这个地区有很多________，上面有很多汽车，人行道上每天都有很多人。这个地区________很贵，商店很多，很多人在商店工作。

厕所　警察局

2) ________在火车站对面，很近。你丢了东西，可以在那里得到帮助。________在火车站里，在左边，很干净。

6. Complete the sentences following the examples.

1)

我	在	火车站旁边	坐	公共汽车	。
我	在		学习		。
					。

2)

英语课	和	音乐课	都	不很	难	。
	和		都	不很		。
						。

7. Make sentences to describe the pictures by rearranging the words.

1) 我家　很　警察局　离　近

____

2) 大　不　和　很　都　卧室　客厅

____

3) 她　小猫　花园　在　里　找

____

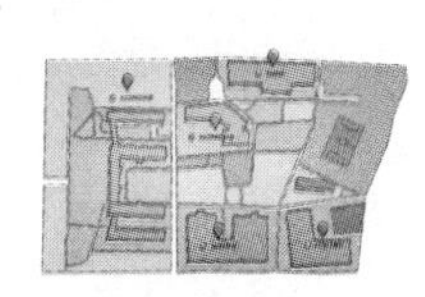

4) 多　这　很　学校　地区　个　的

____

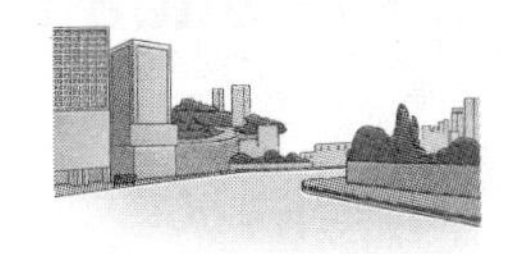

5) 城市　街道　的　干净　这个　很　都

____

8. Answer the following questions according to Exercise 4 of the Student's Book.

1) “我”家在哪儿?

____

2) “我”常常去故宫做什么?

____

3) 市中心的商店东西贵吗? 人多吗?

____

4) 本地人喜欢去剧院看什么？

____

5) 在北京有没有失业的人？

____

9. Find a map of the city or town you live in. Introduce the locations of railway stations, police stations, and well-known hotels.

____

____

____

10. Is it convenient to get around, go shopping, and take public transportation in your city? Try to describe the situation.

____

____

____

11. Fill in the blanks with the correct characters and write a similar paragraph of your own.

我家在一个不大的城市，人不多，可是图书________、电影________、博物________、剧________、邮________都有，我们常常去看书、看电影、看展览、看表演和寄信。教堂和火车________在市中心，也有很多商________和饭________。我喜欢这个城市，很干净，空气很好。

12. Listen and decide True (T) or False (F) .

1) “我”家有很多汽车。(　　)
2) “我”喜欢看地图。(　　)
3) 星期六上午“我”去图书馆看书，下午去体育馆踢足球。(　　)
4) 这个城市很小，可是商店很多。(　　)

13. Pretend you are a tour guide in your city. Describe the features of your city, the famous people or buildings, the environment, and the things you think are most important.

14. Practice writing more characters.

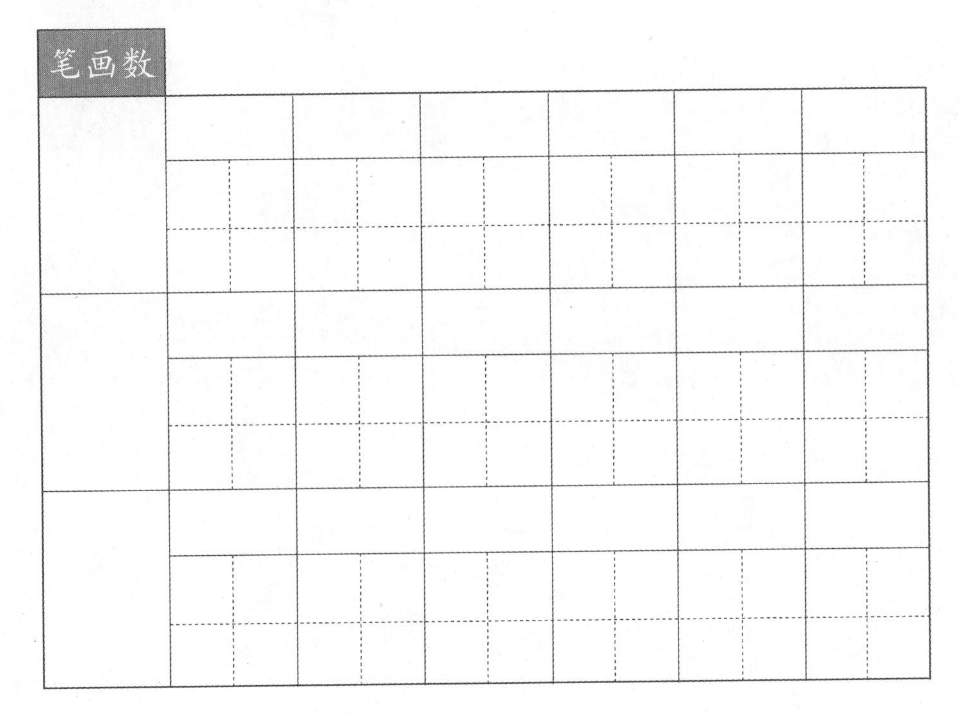

Additional Vocabulary

少	shǎo	few
方便	fāngbiàn	convenient
交通	jiāotōng	traffic
怎么样	zěnmeyàng	how
为什么	wèi shénme	why

Unit Three Home and Shopping

第三单元 家居与购物

第七课 我的新家

1. Write the tones of the words or phrases, then translate them.

xiansheng	fumu	kongtiao	zhu	bingxiang	ceng	canting
先生	父母	空调	住	冰箱	层	餐厅
xiyiji	yushi	yigui	ditan	dao	chaoshi	yiqian
洗衣机	浴室	衣柜	地毯	到	超市	以前

2. Write the characters.

笔画数						
	xiān					
	fù					
	mǔ					

	xǐ					
	kōng					
	dào					

3. Make new words or phrases based on the characters given.

先 xiān	洗 xǐ	空 kōng	浴 yù	以 yǐ
父 fù	生 shēng	衣 yī	母 mǔ	餐 cān
调 tiáo	冰 bīng	地 dì	超 chāo	服 fú
柜 guì	机 jī	市 shì	箱 xiāng	舒 shū
毯 tǎn	衣 yī	室 shì	前 qián	厅 tīng

1) ____________ 2) ____________ 3) ____________

4) ____________ 5) ____________ 6) ____________

7) ____________ 8) ____________ 9) ____________

10) ____________ 11) ____________ 12) ____________

4. Write characters using the following radicals.

氵 ________________________

冫 ________________________

木 ________________________

火 ________________________

5. Fill in the blanks with the given words following the text.

来 从 父母 住

1) 张明______上海______，他______在王先生家。王先生是张明______的好朋友。

舒服 到 层 浴室

2) 张明的房间和______都在二______，很漂亮，也很______，他欢迎我们______他的新家来。

什么 看看 超市 以前

3) 王先生家旁边有一个______。张明想去______，他不想买______。他七点______回来。

6. Complete the sentences following the examples.

1)

我朋友	到	英国	来	学习英语	。
	到		去	看电影	。
				买东西	。
					。

2)

他	给	我	买了	衣柜	和	地毯	。
妈妈			买了		和		。
			准备了				。
							。

7. Make sentences to describe the pictures by rearranging the words.

1) 我们 运动场 下午 足球 要 去 到 踢

___

2) 你们 我 到 来 的 新家 欢迎

___

3) 书架 我 爸爸 给 买 书桌 和 了

___

4) 王先生 张明 他 的 从 来 上海 是 朋友

___

5) 他家 两层 客厅 有 在 一层 二层 餐厅 浴室 在

____

____

8. Choose the correct pictures following the sentences.

1) 李先生是我的朋友，他在超市工作。(　　)

A

B

2) 客厅有地毯，卧室有衣柜，冰箱在厨房，洗衣机在浴室。(　　)

A

B

3) 这个餐厅有空调，夏天不热，冬天不冷，很舒服。(　　)

A

B

4) 他常常到图书馆看书，我给他准备了新自行车。(　　)

A

B

9. Draw a picture of your room. Do you like your room? What do you have in it ?

10. If you could, how would you decorate a room for your best friend? What would you prepare for him or her, and why? You can choose some of the following items to describe.

空调 冰箱 衣柜 洗衣机

餐厅 地毯 书桌 书架 电脑

11. Write something about your house and invite your friends to come over. Try to use the given words or phrases.

我家在……　　离　　我家有……　　……有……

舒服　　欢迎　　到……来……

12. Listen and answer the following questions.

1) "我"家的房子在哪儿?

2) "我"家有几个浴室? 冰箱在哪儿?

3) "我"家旁边有什么? "我"常常到哪儿去买东西?

4) 谁常常来"我"家?

13. Practice writing more characters.

笔画数						

Additional Vocabulary

书桌	shūzhuō	desk
台灯	táidēng	desk lamp
海报	hǎibào	poster
上下床	shàngxiàchuáng	bunk bed
窗帘	chuānglián	curtain
颜色	yánsè	color

第八课　我想送她一个礼物

1. Write the tones of the words or phrases, then translate them.

liwu	taitai	gouwu	ke'ai
礼物	太太	购物	可爱
qingchu	Riben	sunnü	qunzi
清楚	日本	孙女	裙子
baihuo shangchang	geng	yinggai	xian
百货商场	更	应该	先
zhaoxiangji	wen	toufa	wang
照相机	问	头发	忘

2. Write the characters.

笔画数						
	sòng					
	lǐ					

	wù
	qīng
	chǔ
	gèng

3. Make new words or phrases based on the characters given.

日 rì	清 qīng	机 jī	礼 lǐ	应 yīng
可 kě	子 zi	爱 ài	货 huò	发 fà
楚 chǔ	商 shāng	物 wù	购 gòu	物 wù
裙 qún	照 zhào	百 bǎi	女 nǚ	该 gāi
相 xiàng	孙 sūn	本 běn	场 chǎng	头 tóu

1) ______________ 2) ______________ 3) ______________

4) ______________ 5) ______________ 6) ______________

7) ______________ 8) ______________ 9) ______________

10) ______________ 11) ______________

4. Write characters using the following radicals.

子 ______________________

贝 ______________________

礻 ______________________

衤 ______________________

5. Fill in the blanks with the given words following the text.

还 送 生日 礼物 先

1) 马太太有一个孙女，明天是她孙女的________。马太太________去了百货商场，________去了购物中心，她想________孙女一个________。

孙女 裙子 漂亮 照相机

2) 德国的________很有名，马太太买了一个，想送给________。她还买了一条白________，送给Mary，Mary穿一定________极了。

6. Complete the sentences following the examples.

1)

汉语考试	不怎么	难	。
购物中心		远	。
		有名	。
			。

2)

这个	比	那个	更	好	。
小狗		小猫			。
				有意思	。
					。

3)

他	问	我	送什么好	。
爸爸			喜欢什么礼物	。
			哪个照相机有名	。
				。

7. Make sentences to describe the pictures by rearranging the words.

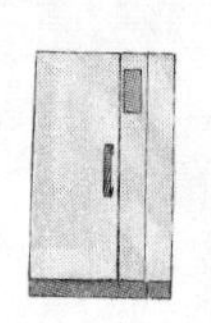

1) 冰箱 德国 的 吧 是 这个

____

2) 百货商场 购物中心 不 和 怎么 都 远

____

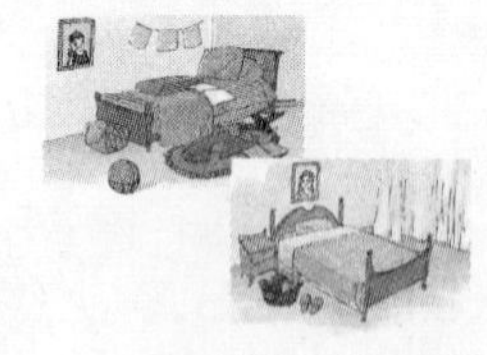

3) 我 姐姐 干净 的 的 更 房间 比

____

4) 孙女 马太太 买 白 一 了 裙子 条 给

____

5) 他 在 我 哪儿 百货商场 问

____

8. Decide True (T) or False (F) according to Exercise 4 of the Student's Book.

1) 马太太的孙女上小学了。(　　)
2) "我"家旁边的百货商场不怎么大。(　　)
3) 哥哥的照相机比姐姐的漂亮。(　　)
4) Ann打电话问我音乐会什么时候开始。(　　)
5) 我们应该先问问马太太喜欢什么礼物。(　　)
6) 王经理的女儿是黄头发，穿了一条白裙子。(　　)

9. Make a birthday card for your friend.

10. Fill in the blanks with the correct characters and write a similar paragraph of your own.

明天是姐姐的________，她今年________岁，她在图书馆________。我们都想送她一个生日________。爸爸________她买了一个照相机，妈妈想________她一个手机。

姐姐喜欢看电影，哥哥要送她一张电影______。我给姐姐做了一条裙子，她一定喜欢。

____

____

____

____

11. Describe one of your birthday parties using the given words or phrases. Include the following information: your date of birth, the location of the party, who were there, what kinds of presents you received, and what activities you participated in.

我的生日是……　给……买了……　送

礼物　还　可爱　……极了　最

____

____

____

____

____

12. Listen and answer the following questions.

1) 明天是谁的生日？

____

2) 百货商场和购物中心哪个更好？

3) “我们”给妈妈买了什么？

4) 姐姐买了什么？“我”买了什么？

13. Practice writing more characters.

笔画数

Additional Vocabulary

贺卡	hèkǎ	greeting card
祝	zhù	to wish
快乐	kuàilè	happy
晚会	wǎnhuì	party
蛋糕	dàngāo	cake
玩具	wánjù	toy
娃娃	wáwa	doll

第九课　他买到了纪念品

1. Write the tones of the words or phrases, then translate them.

qing	shangchang	qizi	yingbang	yizhi	rang	youpiao	jinianpin
请	商场	妻子	英镑	一直	让	邮票	纪念品
huan	shudian	zhangfu	guohua	sunzi	dao	yixie	renminbi
换	书店	丈夫	国画	孙子	到	一些	人民币

2. Write the characters.

笔画数						
	jì					
	niàn					
	pǐn					

	shāng					
	zhí					
	zǒu					

3. Make new words or phrases based on the characters given.

书 shū	子 zi	场 chǎng	一 yī	子 zi
票 piào	些 xiē	孙 sūn	商 shāng	妻 qī
纪 jì	邮 yóu	人 rén	直 zhí	店 diàn
品 pǐn	念 niàn	币 bì	一 yī	民 mín

1) ____________ 2) ____________ 3) ____________

4) ____________ 5) ____________ 6) ____________

7) ____________ 8) ____________ 9) ____________

4. Write characters using the following radicals.

纟 ______________________________

心 ______________________________

辶 ______________________________

5. Fill in the blanks with the given words following the text.

中文　英国　国画　商场　一些

1) 我和王先生一起去________买纪念品和礼物，因为他快要回________了。他买了________和很多________书，还买了________中国邮票，他很高兴。

离　买到了　买不到　买得到

2) 王先生在这个商场________中国有名的国画。可是，这个商场________中文书，在书店________。书店________这个商场不远。

6. Complete the sentences following the examples.

1)

他	买到了	喜欢的画	。
	看到了	漂亮的风景	。
		中国唱片	。
			。

2)

在	这个商场	买得到	国画	，	买不到	中文书	。
	这个房间		街道	，		海滩	。
			英国茶			中国茶	。
							。

3)

他	请	我	跟他一起去买风筝	。
			去剧院看京剧	。
		朋友		。
				。

7. Make sentences to describe the pictures by rearranging the words.

1) 王先生 国画 了 喜欢 买 的 到 最

____

2) 他 飞机票 火车 没买到 去 坐 所以 他

____

3) 我 姐姐 她 请 一起 看 去 跟 电影

____

4) 商场 纪念品 水果 在 可是 这个 买得到 买不到

____

5) 书店 公园 不 这个 一直 远 走 离

____

8. Answer the following questions according to Exercise 4 of the Student's Book.

1) "我"在中国买了什么？

____

2) "我"喜欢什么？

____

3) "我"星期六请朋友做什么？

____

4) 在哪儿看不到这个演员的电影？

____

9. Draw a picture of your school's mascot and some souvenirs from your school. Which one(s) do you recommend?

10. Fill in the blanks with the correct characters and write a similar paragraph of your own.

今年________我和爸爸妈妈一起去了中国。我们去了很多地方，我最喜欢的是北京。我在北京买了很多________，还买到了我最喜欢的中国画。成龙是中国有名的________演员，可是我没看________他。

____

____

____

____

11. Listen and answer the following questions.

1) 今年冬天“我”去了什么地方？买了什么？

____

2) “我”喜欢谁？

____

3) 谁在百货商场工作？他的孙子是老师吗？

____

4) 朋友送了“我”什么礼物？

____

12. Presentation: Bring a souvenir you have to class and introduce it to your classmates. You should give the following information.

1) What is it?
2) When and where did you get it?
3) Why did you choose it?

13. Practice writing more characters.

笔画数						

Additional Vocabulary

风筝	fēngzheng	kite
吉祥物	jíxiángwù	mascot
T恤衫	T xù shān	T-shirt
帽子	màozi	hat; cap
丝绸	sīchóu	silk
冰箱贴	bīngxiāngtiē	refrigerator magnet
钥匙扣	yàoshikòu	key ring
书签	shūqiān	bookmarker
丝巾	sījīn	silk scarf
领带	lǐngdài	necktie
特色	tèsè	characteristic
各种各样	gèzhǒng-gèyàng	various; all kinds of

第十课 你说汉语说得真好

1. Write the tones of the words or phrases, then translate them.

laoshi	hanzi	lianxi	tongxue	xie	nuli	jianglai
老师	汉字	练习	同学	写	努力	将来
huida	wenti	keben	biye	dui	qingnianren	ji
回答	问题	课本	毕业	对	青年人	记

2. Write the characters.

笔画数						
	hàn					
	xiě					
	wèn					

	dá					
	tí					
	qǐng					

3. Make new words or phrases based on the characters given.

汉 hàn	回 huí	老 lǎo	业 yè	将 jiāng
习 xí	毕 bì	字 zì	问 wèn	兴 xìng
答 dá	本 běn	练 liàn	同 tóng	来 lái
学 xué	题 tí	师 shī	课 kè	趣 qù

1) ______ 2) ______ 3) ______

4) ______ 5) ______ 6) ______

7) ______ 8) ______ 9) ______ 10) ______

4. Write characters using the following radicals.

又 ______

氵 ______

⺮ ______

5. Fill in the blanks with the given words following the text.

上 做 写 考试 毕业

1) 我快要中学________了，现在准备________。我们都学习汉语，________汉语课很有意思。我们的老师每天跟我们一起________汉字、________练习。

中学 问题 得 说

2) 我们是美国________的学生，我们的汉语老师是美国人。她写汉字写________很漂亮，________汉语说得很好。我们班的同学都喜欢说汉语，也喜欢回答老师的________。

难 去 坐

3) 除了北京，他还要________上海。可是去上海的火车票很________买，所以他________飞机去。

6. Complete the sentences following the examples.

1)

他	说	汉语	说	得	很好	。
	写	汉字			不太好	。
		国画				。
						。

2)

火车票	很	难	买	。
	不	难	学	。
		难	回答	。
				。

3)

这个问题	不	难	回答	。
	不	难	写	。
			买	。
				。

4)

他	对	中国画	很有兴趣	。
	对		很有兴趣	。
	对		没有兴趣	。
				。

7. Make sentences to describe the pictures by rearranging the words.

1) 篮球 老师 好 打 打 很 的 得 他

____

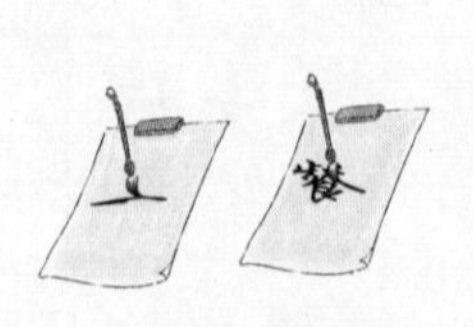

2) 这个 那个 写 写 汉字 汉字 难 难 很 不

____

3) 问题 清楚 回答 回答 得 很 他

____

4) 课本 练习 这个 难 不 上 的 做

____

8. Decide True (T) or False (F) according to Exercise 4 of the Student's Book.

1) 小红会打乒乓球，不会打篮球。(　　)
2) 我的朋友写汉字写得很漂亮。(　　)
3) 妈妈坐飞机去广州。(　　)
4) 学习汉语的时候，我喜欢问问题。(　　)
5) 我哥哥对学习汉语没有兴趣。(　　)

9. Fill in the school timetable. Which subject do you like or dislike?

	星期一	星期二	星期三	星期四	星期五
一					
二					
三					
四					
五					

10. Fill in the blanks with the correct characters and write a similar paragraph of your own.

我在北京国际学校（xuéxiào, school）________。我的________有美国人、英国人、德国人、日本人，也有中国人，我们一起学习。我们有很多课，________课、________课和________课。我喜欢上汉语课。我们的汉语老师是中国人，他说英语________得很好，我们喜欢问他很多问题，他回答问题________得很清楚。我们常常一起做练习、写汉字。他说我写汉字________得很漂亮。我真高兴。

____

____

____

____

11. Try to use some of the given words or phrases to introduce your Chinese class, teacher, and classmates.

老师　同学　毕业　说汉语说得……　汉字　回答

问题　真　越来越　对……有兴趣　努力　将来

____

____

____

____

____

12. Listen and answer the following questions.

1) 谁在北京学习汉语?

____

2) “我”的老师是哪国人?

____

3) “我”的老师对什么有兴趣?

____

4) “我”有中国同学吗?

____

5) 现在“我”的汉语好吗?

____

13. Describe one of your classmates. Ask your partner to guess whom you are talking about. Do not mention his or her appearance but talk about what he or she is good at, what his or her favourite subjects are, interests and hobbies, and what he or she would like to do in the future.

14. Practice writing more characters.

笔画数						

Additional Vocabulary

学校	xuéxiào	school
周末	zhōumò	weekend
夏令营	xiàlìngyíng	summer camp
小组	xiǎozǔ	group
对话	duìhuà	dialogue; conversation
讨论	tǎolùn	to discuss

第十一课　比赛四点才开始

1. Write the tones of the words or phrases, then translate them.

xingqitian	huodong	xiju	kanbing	dui	duiyuan	renshi
星期天	活动	戏剧	看病	队	队员	认识
kai(men)	fashao	yaoshi	ticao	cai	xiwang	yijing
开(门)	发烧	要是	体操	才	希望	已经

2. Write the characters.

笔画数						
	huó					
	shāo					
	cāo					
	xì					

	cái					
	duì					

3. Make new words or phrases based on the characters given.

体	tǐ	发	fā	剧	jù	活	huó	员	yuán
戏	xì	经	jīng	病	bìng	操	cāo	望	wàng
是	shì	烧	shāo	识	shí	看	kàn	已	yǐ
队	duì	动	dòng	要	yào	认	rèn	希	xī

1) ____________ 2) ____________ 3) ____________

4) ____________ 5) ____________ 6) ____________

7) __________ 8) __________ 9) __________ 10) __________

4. Write characters using the following radicals.

日 ______________________________

阝 ______________________________

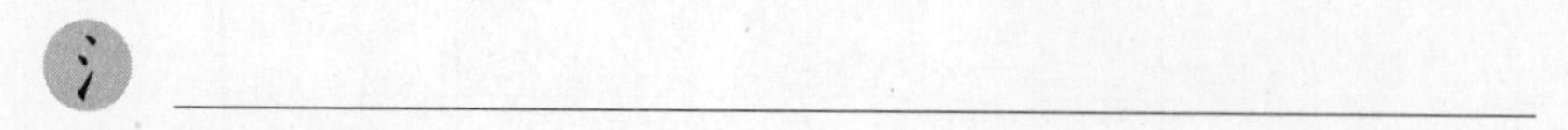

5. Fill in the blanks with the given words following the text.

队　在　要是　星期天　队员

1) 这个______，我们学校的戏剧队______礼堂表演。除了戏剧______，我们还有篮球队、足球队、乒乓球队和体操队。我哥哥是足球队的______。______天气好，他们就训练。

看看　没有　开始　才

2) 篮球比赛现在没有______，比赛四点______开始。可是，明明______来，他发烧，去看病了。我们晚上要去______他。

6. Complete the sentences following the examples.

1)

购物中心	十点	才	开门	。
	五十岁		学习开车	。
			睡觉	。
				。

2)

要是	天气好	我	就	去	。
	来北京	你		给我打电话	。
				买国画	。
					。

3)

现在	已经	三点	了	。
	已经	开始	了	。
		不发烧		。
				。

7. Make sentences to describe the pictures by rearranging the words.

1) 开始　训练　三点半　体操队　才

____

2) 八点　吃饭　电影　开始　现在　去
才　吧

____

3) 戏剧　喜欢　我们　你　要是　就　去
不　听　音乐会

____

4) 星期天　学校　活动　要是　就　我们
没有　去　海滩

____

8. Answer the following questions according to Exercise 4 of the Student's Book.

1) “我们”星期几去打乒乓球？几点去？

____

2) 今天“我们”在学校表演什么？

____

3) “我”的朋友昨天不舒服吗？

____

4) 国家博物馆有新的展览吗？博物馆几点开门？

____

9. Design a poster for a sporting match or an artistic performance.

10. Try to use some of the given words or phrases to talk about your favourite extra-curricular activities.

……队 活动 除了……还…… 要是……就……

常常 表演 比赛 欢迎

11. Listen and answer the following questions.

1) 小海在哪儿学习？

2) 乒乓球队在哪儿训练？

3) 丽丽是谁？她是乒乓球队的吗？

4) 小海和同学这个星期天做什么？

12. Pretend you are the captain of a sports team or an artistic group. Give a speech to recruit new members. Your speech should include information about what your team is, your team's achievement, and the requirements of new recruits.

13. Practice writing more characters.

笔画数

Additional Vocabulary

棒球	bàngqiú	baseball
橄榄球	gǎnlǎnqiú	rugby
健身房	jiànshēnfáng	gym
课余活动	kèyú huódòng	after-school activities
话剧	huàjù	modern drama; stage play
芭蕾舞	bālěiwǔ	ballet
踢踏舞	tītàwǔ	tap dance

第十二课 看看我的电子邮件

1. Write the tones of the words or phrases, then translate them.

xin	xiaoxue	biyou	kunnan	shangwang	gongsi	gaosu
信	小学	笔友	困难	上网	公司	告诉
cuo	xueqi	Dewen	bangzhu	chengnianren	wangye	wangzhi
错	学期	德文	帮助	成年人	网页	网址

2. Write the characters.

笔画数						
	chéng					
	cuò					
	kùn					
	nán					

	bāng				
	zhù				

3. Make new words or phrases based on the characters given.

网 wǎng	难 nán	纸 zhǐ	友 yǒu	司 sī
小 xiǎo	笔 bǐ	告 gào	学 xué	诉 sù
帮 bāng	报 bào	困 kùn	学 xué	页 yè
助 zhù	网 wǎng	期 qī	公 gōng	址 zhǐ

1) ______________ 2) ______________ 3) ______________

4) ______________ 5) ______________ 6) ______________

7) ____________ 8) ____________ 9) ____________ 10) ____________

4. Write characters using the following radicals.

耳 ____

门 ____

氵 ____

5. Fill in the blanks with the given words following the text.

上　信　新闻　小学　笔友

1) 明明的妹妹是_______的学生，她喜欢网_______的游戏。明明的爸爸喜欢看网上的_______。明明除了看新闻，还喜欢写_______，他在网上有一个_______，是德国人。

看看　电子　成年　都　有

2) 小红想看新闻，可是明明想_______网上的电子邮件。因为明明的笔友常常给他写_______邮件。明明的笔友_______中国人，也有英国人和德国人，他们不_______是中学的学生，也有_______人。

6. Complete the sentences following the examples.

1)

我	想	看看	报	。
	要	听听		。
			比赛	。
				。

2)

我	跟	爸爸	一样	喜欢	看新闻	。
		妹妹			问问题	。
					购物	。
						。

7. Make sentences to describe the pictures by rearranging the words.

1) 妈妈　爸爸　看　跟　京剧　喜欢　中国　一样

____

2) 现在　我们　看看　新闻　七点　吧

____

3) 我　我　同学　要是　就　困难　帮助　有

____

4) 爸爸　买　上　今天　在　了　网　电影票

____

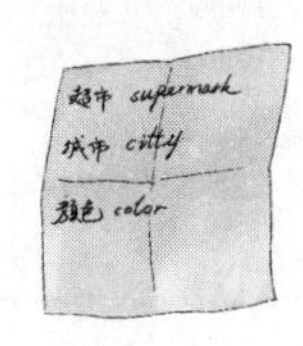

5) 中文　英文　写　写　对　可是　我　的　了　了　错

____

8. Decide True (T) or False (F) according to Exercise 4 of the Student's Book.

1) “我们”班的同学跟“我”一样喜欢写汉字。(　　)
2) “我”跟妹妹一样打乒乓球打得很好。(　　)
3) “我”常常上网看美国篮球队比赛的新闻。(　　)
4) “我”常常在网上给笔友写信。(　　)

9. Write an e-mail to your friend in Chinese.

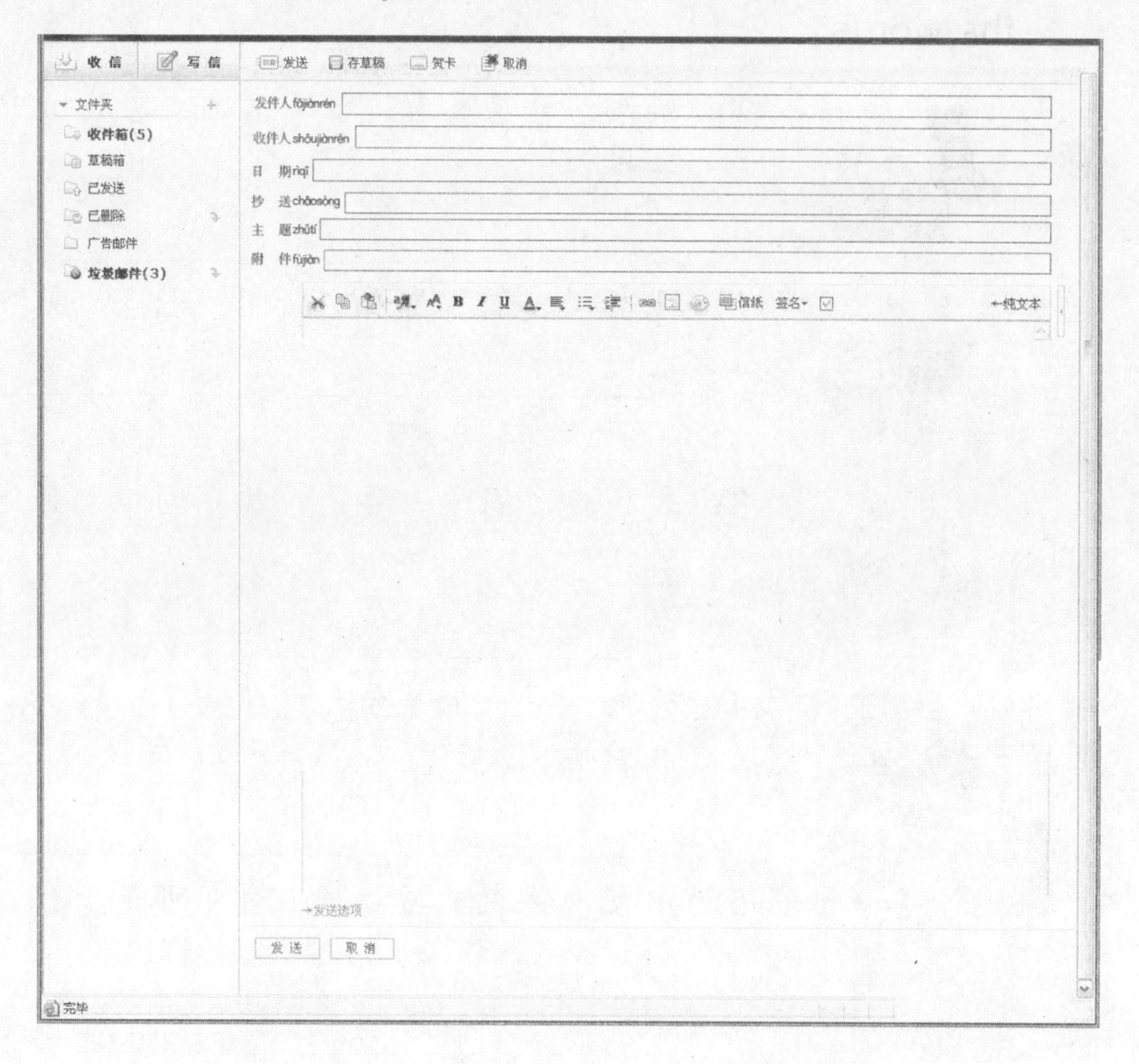

10. Try to use some of the given words or phrases to talk about what you use the computer and the Internet for.

电脑　电脑游戏　上网　除了……，还……

笔友　要是……，就……　网页　网址

11. Listen and answer the following questions.

1) 爸爸做什么工作？他喜欢什么？

2) “我”喜欢什么？

3) 谁跟“我”一样喜欢听音乐？

4) 谁的爱好跟“我”不一样？

5) 谁喜欢电脑游戏？

12. Discuss your experience with online learning with your partner. How often do you surf the Internet, what are your experiences learning Chinese online, what do your friends talk about online, and what are some useful Chinese study websites?

13. Practice writing more characters.

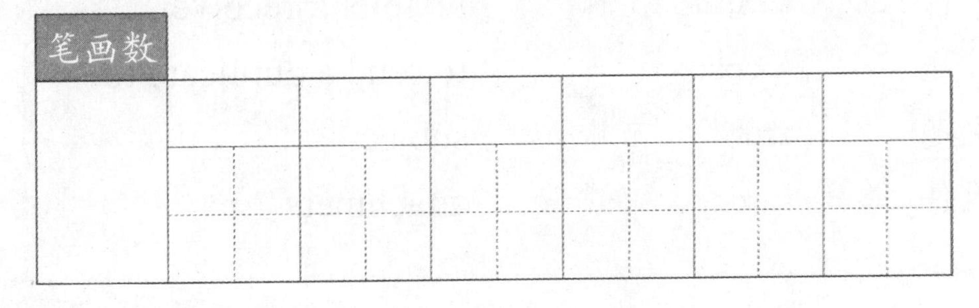

Additional Vocabulary

聊天儿	liáotiānr	to chat
网上购物	wǎng shang gòuwù	online shopping
下载	xiàzài	to download
博客	bókè	blog
网名	wǎngmíng	net name; cyber-name
发件人	fājiànrén	sender
收件人	shōujiànrén	recipient; receiver
抄送	chāosòng	to send a duplicate to
主题	zhǔtí	subject
附件	fùjiàn	attachment

第十三课 他从来没吃过中药

1. Write the tones of the words or phrases, then translate them.

bizi	houlong	kesou	shangfeng	erduo	shou	jiao
鼻子	喉咙	咳嗽	伤风	耳朵	手	脚
zhongyao	xiyao	yachi	kaishui	keneng	bei	wei
中药	西药	牙齿	开水	可能	背	胃

2. Write the characters.

笔画数						
	ěr					
	yá					
	bèi					

	wèi					
	jiǎo					
	yào					

3. Make new words or phrases based on the characters given.

开 kāi	喉 hóu	房 fáng	齿 chǐ	鼻 bí
牙 yá	来 lái	咳 ké	伤 shāng	址 zhǐ
风 fēng	朵 duǒ	从 cóng	咙 lóng	子 zi
药 yào	嗽 sòu	水 shuǐ	耳 ěr	地 dì

1) ________ 2) ________ 3) ________

4) ________ 5) ________ 6) ________

7) ________ 8) ________ 9) ________ 10) ________

4. Write characters using the following radicals.

艹 ________________________________

口 ________________________________

月 ________________________________

木 ________________________________

5. Fill in the blanks with the given words following the text.

病　疼　西药　学校　医院　中药

1) 明明今天________了，他没去________。明明的胃________得很，他去了________。药房里有________，也有________。

吃　好　喝　伤风　头　休息　可能

2) 小红________了，________疼极了，喉咙也疼，在家________。妈妈给她________了药，也给她________了很多开水。要是她明天________了，________就去上课。

6. Complete the sentences following the examples.

1)

他	的	胃	疼	得	很	。
小红		头		得	很	。
小海		喉咙		得		。
						。

2)

我	从来	没	吃	过	中药	。
明明		没	去		伦敦	。
他			看		这个电影	。
						。

7. Make sentences to describe the pictures by rearranging the words.

1) 我 飞机 没 过 坐 从来

____

2) 哥哥 昨天 我 和 都 病 了

____

3) 小美 很 得 喉咙 疼

____

4) 多 喝水 了 伤风 应该

____

5) 好了 就 明天 你 去 上课 要是

____

6) 我 很 疼 的 头 了 伤风 可能

____

8. Answer the following questions according to Exercise 4 of the Student's Book.

1) 昨天“我”吃了什么？今天“我”好了吗？

____

2) “我”吃过中药吗？“我”想试试什么？

____

3) 现在“我”要去哪儿？

____

4) 小红今天为什么没来学校？

____

9. Talk about yourself using the given prompts.

	疼/不疼
头	今天我的头不疼。
眼睛	
鼻子	
耳朵	
牙齿	昨天我的牙齿疼得很。
嗓子/喉咙	
胃/肚子	
背	
手	
脚	

10. Draw a picture using the words given.

眼睛

鼻子

耳朵

牙齿

头发

喉咙

胃

背

手

脚

11. Fill in the blanks with the correct characters and write a similar paragraph of your own.

我可能________了，昨天开始头________，喉咙也________得很，还咳嗽。妈妈给我吃了________，我说我不用去医院________。我________了很多牛奶。今天________昨天那么________了。今天我没________学校。要是明天我________了，就________上课。

12. Listen and draw lines to connect the following columns.

爷爷	不常生病
妈妈	胃疼
我	头疼
妹妹	耳朵不好

13. Practice writing more characters.

笔画数

Additional Vocabulary

药店	yàodiàn	pharmacy; chemist
嘴	zuǐ	mouth
腿	tuǐ	leg
上学	shàngxué	to go to school
请假	qǐngjià	to ask for leave
病假	bìngjià	sick leave

第十四课　我的身体越来越好

1. Write the tones of the words or phrases, then translate them.

chongwu	shenti	jiawu	ai	shao	jiankang	youyong
宠物	身体	家务	矮	少	健康	有用
shou	zhongtou	qi ma	lao	pang	chabuduo	jiu
瘦	钟头	骑马	老	胖	差不多	就

2. Write the characters.

笔画数	
	zhōng
	mǎ
	jiā
	pàng

	shēn					
	jiù					

3. Make new words or phrases based on the characters given.

体 tǐ	人 rén	起 qǐ	床 chuáng	健 jiàn
马 mǎ	物 wù	身 shēn	动 dòng	用 yòng
头 tóu	运 yùn	备 bèi	骑 qí	有 yǒu
准 zhǔn	老 lǎo	宠 chǒng	钟 zhōng	康 kāng

1) ______________ 2) ______________ 3) ______________

4) ______________ 5) ______________ 6) ______________

7) ____________ 8) ____________ 9) ____________ 10) ____________

4. Write characters using the following radicals.

钅 ____

宀 ____

月 ____

亠 ____

5. Fill in the blanks with the given words following the text.

公园　湖边　家务　老少　骑马　钟头　健康

1) 我家的男女________都喜欢运动。爷爷每天去________打太极拳。奶奶在________散步，爸爸每个星期去________。妈妈每天除了做________以外，还做两个________的运动，妈妈的身体很________。

常常　打　就　胖　有用　喜欢　要是

2) 我很________运动。我很________，________我天天运动，________会越来越瘦了。我________游泳，也常常________篮球。运动对我很________。

6. Complete the sentences following the examples.

1)

他	每天	做	两个	钟头	的	运动	。
爸爸		看	半个		的	报	。
奶奶		打				太极拳	。
							。

2)

我	每天	早上	差不多	六点	就	去	打	篮球	。
妈妈		早上		七点			做	早饭	。
弟弟		下午						电视	。
									。

7. Make sentences to describe the pictures by rearranging the words.

1) 做　钟头　运动　每天　她　几个　的

____

2) 不　你　喜　喜欢　运动

____

3) 爸爸　工作　就　每天　七点半　去

____

4) 打　要是　常常　篮球　高　就　了　越来越

____

5) 踢　我　不　足球　太瘦了　我　因为

____

6) 有用　对　运动　健康　很

____

7) 孩子　这个　六岁　差不多　了

____

8. Answer the following questions according to Exercise 4 of the Student's Book.

1) "我"家的男女老少喜欢什么？"我们"一起去看什么？

____

2) 每天“我”看多长时间网上的新闻？写多长时间的电子邮件？

____

3) “我”请你一起去做什么？购物中心离“我”家远吗？

____

4) “我”每个星期学习骑马多长时间？

____

5) 怎么做对健康很有用？

____

9. Introduce your family's favourite sports.

爷爷	
奶奶	
爸爸	
妈妈	
哥哥	
姐姐	
弟弟	
妹妹	
我	

10. Fill in the blanks with the correct characters and write a similar paragraph of your own.

你要问我喜_______喜欢运动，我当然（dāngrán, of course）喜欢了。我每天_______一个小时的运动。昨天下午我去体育馆游泳了。我______三点就去了，体育馆里有很多人，男女老少都有。你______不准备运动？要是你准备运动，我请你明天______我一起去游泳，好吗？运动对健康很______。

____

____

____

11. Listen and draw lines to connect the following columns.

奶奶	骑马
爸爸	踢足球
妈妈	散步
我和哥哥	游泳

12. Practice writing more characters.

笔画数						

Additional Vocabulary

骑车	qí chē	to ride a bicycle
减肥	jiǎnféi	on a diet
健身	jiànshēn	bodybuilding
家庭	jiātíng	family
习惯	xíguàn	habit
动物	dòngwù	animal

第十五课　我们都爱吃她做的点心

1. Write the tones of the words or phrases, then translate them.

zaofan	wufan	wanfan	he jiu	hen jiu	tang
早饭	午饭	晚饭	喝酒	很久	汤
ai	zhu	chao	hezui	zhongwu	wan
爱	煮	炒	喝醉	中午	碗

2. Write the characters.

笔画数						
	zhǔ					
	ài					
	wǎn					
	hē					

	chǎo					
	jiǔ					

3. Make new words or phrases based on the characters given.

醉	zuì	喝	hē	饭	fàn	午	wǔ
心	xīn	吃	chī	喝	hē	久	jiǔ
酒	jiǔ	饭	fàn	中	zhōng	晚	wǎn
饭	fàn	早	zǎo	点	diǎn	很	hěn

1) ________ 2) ________ 3) ________ 4) ________

5) ________ 6) ________ 7) ________ 8) ________

4. Write characters using the following radicals.

口 ____________________

灬 ____________________

饣 ____________________

氵 ____________________

5. Fill in the blanks with the given words following the text.

炒　吃饭　喝　晚饭　早饭　煮　中午

1) 我是一个中学的学生，学校离我家很近，所以我差不多每天在家______。我的______有鸡蛋、牛奶和面包。我不______咖啡。午饭我喜欢吃妈妈______的米饭，______我妈妈不上班。______我常常吃面条儿。我妈妈______的菜很好吃。

爱　饭　好吃　喝酒　很久　喝醉　也

2) 在我的家里，我妈妈做饭。我们都______吃她做的______。我爸爸______会做饭，可是他炒的菜很不______。他______没有做饭了。爸爸爱______，他每天晚上都喝酒，可是他喝得不多，从来没______过。

6. Complete the sentences following the examples.

1)

我	也	吃	肉	，	也	吃	菜	。
妈妈		煮	米饭	，		炒	菜	。
爸爸			报纸	，			电视	。
				，				。

2)

我们	都爱	吃	妈妈	做	的	点心	。
学生们		听	老师	说		汉语	。
很多人		看				电影	。
							。

3)

他	很久	没有	做	饭	了	。
爸爸			喝	酒	了	。
妈妈				太极拳		。
						。

7. Make sentences to describe the pictures by rearranging the words.

1) 吃过　没有　你　中国菜

____

2) 我　打　也　篮球　踢　足球

____

3) 好吃　的　哥哥　早饭　做　不

____

4) 的　汉字　好看　很　老师　写

____

5) 爱 吃 的 都 面条儿 我们 意大利人 做

____

6) 上网 哥哥 没有 很久 了

____

8. Answer the following questions according to Exercise 4 of the Student's Book.

1) 学校离"我"家远吗?"我"每天在哪里吃午饭?

____

2) "我"会做中国菜吗?"我"做的中国菜好吃吗?

____

3) "我"常跟朋友一起去做什么?

____

4) "我们"在中秋节吃什么?

____

5) "我"中午想吃什么?

____

6) 妈妈做的汤好喝吗?妈妈最近(zuìjìn, recently)做汤了吗?

____

9. Draw a picture based on the phrases given.

妈妈做的蔬菜 奶奶做的点心
爸爸炒的牛肉 爷爷煮的饭
哥哥买的冰激凌（bīngjīlíng, ice cream）

10. Fill in the blanks with the correct characters and write a similar paragraph of your own.

在我们家里，妈妈和爸爸_______做饭，妈妈做的早饭很好吃，我和哥哥都喜欢吃。中午我们都不回家吃午饭，我和哥哥在学校吃午饭，妈妈和爸爸_______办公室吃午饭。我们都回家吃晚饭，我们都喜欢吃爸爸炒_______中国菜，我们吃青菜，_______吃肉。我们很久没吃妈妈炒的菜了。

____

____

____

11. Listen and decide True (T) or False (F).

1) 爸爸喝葡萄酒。(　　)
2) 妈妈喝红茶，也喝绿茶。(　　)
3) “我”和哥哥不喜欢吃冰激凌。(　　)

12. Practice writing more characters.

笔画数						

Additional Vocabulary

葡萄酒	pútaojiǔ	wine
绿茶	lǜchá	green tea
红茶	hóngchá	red tea
炒面	chǎomiàn	*chow mein* (stir-fried noodles with shredded meat and vegetables)
有时	yǒushí	sometimes
意大利	Yìdàlì	Italy

Unit Six Entertainment and Leisure

第六单元 娱乐与休闲

第十六课 熊猫可爱极了

1. Write the tones of the words or phrases, then translate them.

shengqi	mingxinpian	xiongmao	qilai	zhan
生气	明信片	熊猫	起来	站
shichang	dongwuyuan	yanjing	guolai	huai
市场	动物园	眼镜	过来	坏

2. Write the characters.

笔画数						
	xióng					
	māo					
	zhàn					

	xìn					
	hòu					
	huài					

3. Make new words or phrases based on the characters given.

动 dòng	场 chǎng	可 kě	生 shēng	镜 jìng
起 qǐ	片 piàn	物 wù	明 míng	眼 yǎn
信 xìn	猫 māo	来 lái	市 shì	气 qì
病 bìng	园 yuán	爱 ài	熊 xióng	生 shēng

1) ________ 2) ________ 3) ________

4) ________ 5) ________ 6) ________

7) ________ 8) ________ 9) ________

4. Write characters using the following radicals.

疒 ________

辶 ________

犭 ________

亻 ________

5. Fill in the blanks with the given words following the text.

极　看　去　只

1) 我们城市的动物园里有两______熊猫。星期六我和朋友______动物园______熊猫了。熊猫可爱______了！

高兴　过来　站

2) 熊猫开始做游戏了，孩子们都跑______。看熊猫的人越来越多，后边的孩子都______起来了，孩子们______得不得了。

跟　市场　一样

3) 我和朋友去______买熊猫的明信片，我们买了很多明信片。朋友______我______喜欢熊猫。

一起　新的　坏了

4) 我的眼镜______，我得买______。你跟我______去市场吗？

6. Complete the sentences following the examples.

1)

熊猫	可爱	极了	！
明信片	漂亮		！
奶奶做的菜			！
			！

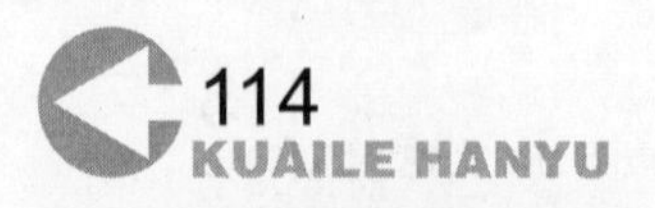

2)

我	和	朋友	去	动物园	看熊猫	了	。
小明		爸爸		体育馆	游泳		。
妈妈				市场			。
							。

3)

回家	的	时候	，	我们	去买	明信片	。
开车			，	我	听	中国音乐	。
看熊猫			，				。
							。

7. Make sentences to describe the pictures by rearranging the words.

1) 了　可爱　极　孩子们

____

2) 和　了　买　明信片　朋友　去　市场　我

____

3) 的时候 去 我们 熊猫 已经 了 开始 吃饭

____

4) 都　孩子们　了　起来　站

____

5) 地　高兴　过来　跑　小狗

6) 新　眼镜　去　商店　买　我

8. Choose the correct pictures following the sentences.

1) 动物园里有两只熊猫，熊猫从中国来。(　　)

A

B

2) 我常常跟爷爷一起去看京剧，看京剧的时候，我们高兴极了。(　　)

A

B

3) 听音乐会的时候，朋友买了很多中国音乐的CD。(　　)

B

4) 我去动物园的时候，熊猫正在睡觉。(　　)

A

B

9. Draw pictures based on the phrases given.

动物园

熊猫

孩子们

站起来

鼓掌（gǔzhǎng）

海豚（hǎitún）

鳄鱼（èyú）

猴子（hóuzi）

长颈鹿（chángjǐnglù）

熊（xióng）

10. Fill in the blanks with the correct characters and write a similar paragraph of your own.

动物园里有很多动物，有两只从中国来的熊猫，可爱__________，男女老少都喜欢熊猫。星期天，爸爸跟我们__________去看熊猫。我们去的时候，熊猫生病了，弟弟很生气。爸爸__________我们买了熊猫的明信片，明信片漂亮极了，我很喜欢。

____

____

____

11. Listen and answer the following questions.

1) 动物园里有几只熊猫？熊猫从哪里来？

____

2) “我”跟谁一起去看京剧？

____

3) 听音乐会的时候，Mike买了什么？

____

4) “我”看过熊猫吗？“我”去动物园的时候，熊猫怎么了？

____

12. Practice writing more characters.

笔画数						

Additional Vocabulary

演出	yǎnchū	to perform; performance
鼓掌	gǔzhǎng	to clap
熊	xióng	bear
猴子	hóuzi	monkey
海豚	hǎitún	dolphin
鳄鱼	èyú	crocodile
游乐园	yóulèyuán	amusement park

第十七课　我们都在图书馆看书

1. Write the tones of the words or phrases, then translate them.

zhong	chuang	zhiwu	yihou	he	kexue
钟	窗	植物	以后	河	科学
nei	qiao	yuedu	chuqu	zhuan	guan deng
内	桥	阅读	出去	转	关灯

2. Write the characters.

笔画数						
	zhí					
	jǐng					
	jì					

	dú					
	hé					
	qiáo					

3. Make new words or phrases based on the characters given.

出 chū	书 shū	鸭 yā	子 zi	学 xué
技 jì	植 zhí	科 kē	阅 yuè	灯 dēng
以 yǐ	书 shū	馆 guǎn	去 qù	科 kē
读 dú	图 tú	后 hòu	物 wù	关 guān

1) ____________ 2) ____________ 3) ____________

4) ____________ 5) ____________ 6) ____________

7) __________ 8) __________ 9) __________ 10) __________

4. Write characters using the following radicals.

氵 ______________________________

禾 ______________________________

木 ______________________________

牛 ______________________________

5. Fill in the blanks with the given words following the text.

阅读 科技 常常

1) 我们学校的图书馆里有很多书。我______在图书馆______书。我喜欢______。

在 以后 都

2) 我的同学们都喜欢去图书馆。下课______，谁______不回家，我们都______图书馆看书。

里 旁边 外边

3) 图书馆______的风景很好。有河、有桥，河______有鸭子，河______有植物，漂亮极了。

转 开 关

4) 我家旁边的商店每天上午9点______门，下午5点______门。从我家______过去就能看见那个商店。

6. Complete the sentences following the examples.

1)

谁	都	喜欢	熊猫	。
谁		想	吃中国菜	。
		不喜欢		。
				。

2)

我们	都	在	图书馆	看书	。
全家人		在	客厅	看电视	。
			运动场	踢足球	。
					。

3)

图书馆	外面	有	公园	，	风景	很	漂亮	。
我家			花园	，		很	好	。
			山	，			美	。
								。

7. Make sentences to describe the pictures by rearranging the words.

1) 都　踢足球　我们　运动场　在

____

2) 常常　地理书　小明　阅读

____

3) 博物馆　花园　外面　一个　有　大

____

4) 很近　湖边　离　我们　学校

____

5) 窗外　大广告　我家　个　有　一

____

6) 出口　过去　能　就　看见　车站　从

____

8. Answer the following questions according to Exercise 4 of the Student's Book.

1) 图书馆每天几点开？“我”家离图书馆远吗？

____

2) 下课后，“我”和朋友们去图书馆看什么？

____

3) 中国国家博物馆外面有什么？风景漂亮吗？

____

4) “我们”学校的图书馆里书多吗？

____

5) 哪个图书馆是中国最大的图书馆？图书馆的书多吗？

____

9. Write a brief introduction about your school's library.

____

____

____

____

____

10. Fill in the blanks with the correct characters and write a similar paragraph of your own.

我家________图书馆很近。图书馆里有很多书，也有很多电脑。下午下课后，我和哥哥________不回家，我们去图书馆看书，也上网。图书馆________门很晚。哥哥阅读科技书，我看网________的新电影，也给朋友发电子邮件。图书馆旁边有一个书店，哥哥常在那里买音乐CD。

____

____

____

11. Listen and fill in the blanks.

1) 我________点半从我家去图书馆。
2) 下课后，我和我的朋友都不________。
3) 国家博物馆外面的风景________极了。
4) 要是你喜欢________，就来我们学校图书馆吧，图书馆里有很多书。
5) 每天有很________人来看书，图书馆的书多极了。

12. Recommend your favourite book to a friend. Discuss how you got the book, a brief plot summary, major characters, and why you like it.

13. Practice writing more characters.

笔画数						

Additional Vocabulary

借书	jiè shū	to borrow a book
文学	wénxué	literature
技术	jìshù	technology
书店	shūdiàn	bookstore
网吧	wǎngbā	Internet café
窗户	chuānghu	window
内部	nèibù	inside
钟表	zhōngbiǎo	clock

第十八课　我们都跑上山去

1. Write the tones of the words or phrases, then translate them.

senlin	xia yu	xingxing	xibian	yun	kou ke	zhongjian
森林	下雨	星星	西边	云	口渴	中间
pa shan	tiankong	taiyang	dalei	kuai	miao	bisai
爬山	天空	太阳	打雷	快	庙	比赛

2. Write the characters.

笔画数						
	pá					
	shān					
	sēn					

	lín					
	yún					
	léi					

3. Make new words or phrases based on the characters given.

边 biān	口 kǒu	打 dǎ	下 xià	间 jiān
天 tiān	林 lín	阳 yáng	森 sēn	风 fēng
雨 yǔ	雷 léi	渴 kě	西 xī	中 zhōng
星 xīng	太 tài	星 xīng	空 kōng	景 jǐng

1) ____________ 2) ____________ 3) ____________

4) ____________ 5) ____________ 6) ____________

7) __________ 8) __________ 9) __________ 10) __________

4. Write characters using the following radicals.

扌 ______________________________

忄 ______________________________

阝 ______________________________

雨 ______________________________

5. Fill in the blanks with the given words following the text.

天气 太阳 爬山

1) 今天我们去______了，可是______不好，没有______。

上 快 从

2) 早上八点，我和朋友开始比赛爬山，我们______山下边跑______山去，我们都跑得很______。

一样 森林 北边

3) 我去______爬山，北边有______也有山，北边的山和西边的山______高。

中间 休息 漂亮

4) 我们在庙里______，庙在山的______，风景很______。

6. Complete the sentences following the examples.

1)

我们	走	下	山	来	。
孩子们		上	楼	去	。
小猫			沙发		。
					。

2)

北边的山	跟	西边的山	一样	高	。
图书馆		博物馆		大	。
这个电影				有意思	。
					。

3)

庙	在	山	的	中间	。
邮局		城市	的		。
服务台		酒店			。
					。

7. Make sentences to describe the pictures by rearranging the words.

1) 都 跑 去 山 上 我们

____

2) 从 山 上边 爷爷 奶奶 下来 走 和

____

3) 很多 天空 有 云 下雨 了 快要

____

4) 的 地理书 多 和 历史书 图书馆 一样

____

5) 火车站 电影院 博物馆 在 中间

____

8. Decide True (T) or False (F) according to Exercise 4 of the Student's Book.

1) 爬山的时候天气很好，太阳很漂亮。(　　)
2) "我们"跑上山去，大家都跑得快极了。(　　)
3) "我"不喜欢在森林里吃饭。(　　)
4) 下雨了，快要刮风了。(　　)
5) 城市北边的山比西边的山高。(　　)
6) 邮局和警察局的中间是火车站。(　　)

9. Write a paragraph to introduce your favourite sports.

____

____

____

____

____

10. Fill in the blanks with the correct characters and write a similar paragraph of your own.

我住在北京。北京的西边和北边________有山，西边的山________北边的山一样高。我和爷爷常去爬山。我们常常跑上山________，在山上吃饭，然后（ránhòu, and then）我们走下山来。我们坐公共汽车回家，公共汽车站在森林的中间。山上空气很好，风景也很漂亮。我越________越喜欢爬山了。

____

____

____

11. Listen and choose the correct picture.

1) A

( )

B

( )

2) A

( )

B

( )

3) A

( )

B

( )

4) A

( )

B

( )

5) A

( )

B

( )

12. Practice writing more characters.

笔画数

Additional Vocabulary

阳光	yángguāng	sunshine
阴天	yīntiān	cloudy sky
下雪	xià xuě	to snow
闪电	shǎndiàn	to lightning
背包	bēibāo	rucksack; knapsack
树林	shùlín	forest
进去	jìnqù	to go in

Unit Seven News and Media

第七单元 新闻与传媒

第十九课 有什么新闻

1. Write the tones of the words or phrases, then translate them.

gongzi	fengsu	zhidao	fangwen	banfa
工资	风俗	知道	访问	办法
jiehun	chou yan	diqiu	dupin	haoxiang
结婚	抽烟	地球	毒品	好像

2. Write the characters.

笔画数						
	fǎng					
	chōu					
	yān					

	dù					
	zhōu					
	zhī					

3. Make new words or phrases based on the characters given.

洲 zhōu	非 fēi	俗 sú	度 dù
访 fǎng	地 dì	美 měi	品 pǐn
知 zhī	道 dào	问 wèn	风 fēng
抽 chōu	资 zī	结 jié	大 dà
球 qiú	洲 zhōu	工 gōng	烟 yān
婚 hūn	印 yìn	毒 dú	学 xué

1) ________ 2) ________ 3) ________

4) ________ 5) ________ 6) ________

7) ________ 8) ________ 9) ________

10) ________ 11) ________ 12) ________

4. Write characters using the following radicals.

阝 ________________

门 ________________

5. Fill in the blanks with the given words following the text.

大　多　高　访问　比赛

1) 今天的新闻很______，一个大学校长要来我们学校______，工人的工资越来越______，污染问题越来越______，中国足球队要去欧洲______。

知道　艺术　开始　展览

2) 我们的博物馆有两个新______，一个是印度结婚风俗展览，一个是非洲艺术展览。我很喜欢______，很想去看非洲艺术展览，可是新闻没说展览什么时候______。我去问问小海，他什么都______。

6. Complete the sentences following the examples.

1)

你	有没有	买	水果	?
		吃	药	?
				?

2)

你	有没有	去	过	那个饭店	?
		学		法语	?
					?

3)

我	什么	都	喜欢吃	。
他			不想说	。
				。

4)

我们的课	越来越	有意思	。
房子		贵	。
			。

7. Make sentences to describe the pictures by rearranging the words.

1) 他 睡觉 有没有 现在

____

2) 你 他 打 电话 有没有 给 过

____

3) 什么 我 问题 没有 都

____

4) 他 博物馆 什么 去 都 过

____

5) 他 身体 瘦 越来越 的

____

8. Answer the following questions according to Exercise 4 of the Student's Book.

1) 爸爸最喜欢看什么电视节目？

2) 新闻里说地球有什么问题？为什么？

3) 现在博物馆有什么展览？还有什么展览快要开始了？

4) 现在很多人喜欢什么工作？为什么？

9. Talk about news that you and your classmates are concerned about.

10. Try to talk about the latest news in Chinese.

11. Fill in the blanks with the correct characters and write a similar paragraph of your own.

本地新闻说，周末有很多人去________山。这个周末天气很好，郊区的山上有很多花，空气也很干净。爬山的人除了本地人，还有很多________别的（biéde, other）地方来的人。大家都________得很高兴。下星期天气也很好，我们都去爬山吧。

____

____

____

12. Listen and answer the following questions.

1) “我们”这个城市有什么问题？

____

2) 网上有什么新闻？

____

3) “我”在网上看到了什么？

____

13. Suppose you and your partner are selecting news for the school's website homepage. You agree on stories about exhibitions, sports, and culture, but disagree on stories about travel, drugs, and smoking. Give reasons for your choices and disagreements.

14. Practice writing more characters.

笔画数					

Additional Vocabulary

价格	jiàgé	price
提高	tígāo	to improve
下降	xiàjiàng	to decline
赢	yíng	to win
输	shū	to lose
发生	fāshēng	to happen
事故	shìgù	accident
受伤	shòushāng	to be injured
死亡	sǐwáng	to die

第二十课 他正在采访

1. Write the tones of the words or phrases, then translate them.

mingren	zhengzai	lingyongqian	caifang	fu	qian
名人	正在	零用钱	采访	付	千
luyinbi	zhangdan	shexiangji	jizhe	hua	wan
录音笔	账单	摄像机	记者	花	万

2. Write the characters.

笔画数						
	jì					
	zhě					
	yòng					
	lù					

	cǎi					
	zhèng					

3. Make new words or phrases based on the characters given.

钱 qián	记 jì	像 xiàng	账 zhàng
访 fǎng	采 cǎi	兼 jiān	钱 qián
职 zhí	零 líng	机 jī	者 zhě
用 yòng	单 dān	摄 shè	赚 zhuàn

1) ____________ 2) ____________ 3) ____________

4) __________ 5) __________ 6) __________ 7) __________

4. Write characters using the following radicals.

耳 ______________________________

贝 ______________________________

5. Fill in the blanks with the given words following the text.

记者 花 采访 网页

1)《学校新闻》是我们学校______上的一个节目，我和明明是这个节目的______。我很喜欢这个工作。今天我们______学生，问他们零用钱怎么______。

给　付　赚

2) 我们每个人都有零用钱，我们兼职______钱，父母也______我们钱。我们用（to use）零用钱买书、买唱片、看电影、跟朋友一起吃饭。吃饭的时候，我们和朋友都______钱。

6. Complete the sentences following the examples.

1)

妈妈	正在	做饭	。
他		做什么	？
			。

2)

我	回家	的时候	，	弟弟	正在	看电视	。
他	打电话			我		睡觉	。
							。

3)

“这个”	汉语	怎么	说	？
“熊猫”	英语			？
				？

7. Make sentences to describe the pictures by rearranging the words.

1) 爷爷　打　正在　太极拳

____

2) 我　他　他　发烧　去　看　正在　时候　的

____

3) 我　她　请　帮助　同学

____

4) 谁　我　他　有　问　照相机

____

5) 问题　回答　个　这　怎么

____

8. Answer the following questions according to Exercise 4 of the Student's Book.

1) 今年生日的时候，"我"的生日礼物有什么？"我"喜欢吗？

____

2) 马先生是什么人？

____

3) "我"的零用钱从哪儿来？

____

4) 跟朋友吃饭的时候，谁付账单？

____

9. Tell your classmates if you are working or volunteering somewhere on or off campus.

____

____

____

10. Fill in the blanks with the correct characters and write a similar paragraph of your own.

电视上有一个节目，这个________的名字叫《每日新闻》。这个节目很________意思，除了爸爸妈妈________，我和姐姐也很喜欢看。今天的新闻说越来越多的人喜欢运动，有的（some）人喜欢跑步，有的人喜欢打球，有的人喜欢学习________太极拳。爸爸很喜欢太极拳，他________知道谁可以教（jiāo, to teach），可是电视新闻没有________。

____

____

____

11. Listen and decide True (T) or False (F).

1) 李先生是本地的名人。(　　)
2) 他在饭馆兼职，每个星期工作十个钟头。(　　)
3) 哥哥的生日礼物是电视。(　　)
4) "我"跟朋友买了很多东西，爸爸替我们付了账单。(　　)

12. Interview three of your classmates about their part-time job and pocket money over the last year. Your questions should include: how much do they get, what do they have to do, how did they get the job, who give them pocket money, and whether they think it is enough.

13. Practice writing more characters.

笔画数

Additional Vocabulary

志愿者	zhìyuànzhě	volunteer
穷人	qióngrén	the poor
捐赠	juānzèng	to donate
玩具	wánjù	toy
社区	shèqū	community

第二十一课　中文歌表演比赛

1. Write the tones of the words or phrases, then translate them.

haoting	xiaojie	huiyuan	baozhi	yong	tiao
好听	小姐	会员	报纸	用	跳
xinyongka	julebu	chang	wei shenme	jiao	wu
信用卡	俱乐部	唱	为什么	教	舞

2. Write the characters.

笔画数						
	gē					
	tiào					
	zhǐ					

	jiāo					
	jiě					
	yuán					

3. Make new words or phrases based on the characters given.

比 bǐ	纸 zhǐ	名 míng	赛 sài	高 gāo	人 rén
报 bào	易 yì	好 hǎo	乐 lè	访 fǎng	用 yòng
兴 xìng	姐 jiě	采 cǎi	者 zhě	信 xìn	有 yǒu
歌 gē	记 jì	听 tīng	唱 chàng	名 míng	容 róng
会 huì	卡 kǎ	小 xiǎo	员 yuán	俱 jù	部 bù

1) ______ 2) ______ 3) ______

4) ______ 5) ______ 6) ______

7) ______ 8) ______ 9) ______

10) ______ 11) ______ 12) ______

13) ______ 14) ______

4. Write characters using the following radicals.

亻 ______

口 ______

5. Fill in the blanks with the given words following the text.

新闻　记者　名人

1) 今天我们学校有一个比赛，每个班都用中文唱歌。很多人来看我们的比赛，有爸爸妈妈、本地的________，报纸的________也来了。明天你看________吧。

请　比　用　教

2) 同学们，我们学校每年都有一个中文歌表演，我们________中文唱歌。中文歌很好听，也不难。我________马小姐________你们唱歌吧，因为她唱歌________我唱得好，她是中文歌俱乐部的会员。

6. Complete the sentences following the examples.

1)

他	用	英语	回答	问题	。
我		录音笔	采访	学生	。

2)

他	爬山	比	我	爬	得	快	。
我	吃饭		弟弟	吃		多	。

3)

他	写汉字	写	得	比	我	漂亮	。
Jim	赚钱	赚			Jack	多	。

7. Make sentences to describe the pictures by rearranging the words.

1) 我　信用卡　付账　用

____

2) 我　他　开　快　开车　比　得

____

3) 我们　我　王先生　学校　请　访问

____

4) 他　会员　网球　俱乐部　是　的

____

5) 我　CD　很　买　的　好听　今天

____

8. Decide True (T) or False (F) according to Exercise 4 of the Student's Book.

1) "我"现在学习汉语学得很好。(　　)

2) 马小姐是一个有名的俱乐部的会员，她正在表演中文歌。(　　)

3) "我"觉得学习中文的好办法是唱中文歌，跳中国舞。(　　)

4) "我们"足球队踢足球踢得不好。(　　)

5) "我们"学校没有骑马俱乐部。(　　)

9. What kind of clubs are there at your school? Are you a member of a club? Which club would you like to join?

____

____

____

10. Fill in the blanks with the correct characters and write a similar paragraph of your own.

我是一个中国国画俱乐部的________。每个星期天我们都有________，看展览、上课、比赛，都很有意思。虽然学习国画的时候很________，可是现在我画得________好。

____

____

____

11. Listen and answer the following questions.

1) “我”有哪些爱好？

____

2) 谁在教“我们”唱中文歌？

____

3) “我”写的新闻在哪里可以看到？

____

4) “我”怎样跟笔友联系？

____

12. Plan a Chinese cultural festival at your school. Your classmates want to perform singing with dancing. Plan the programme including song titles, activities, dress, and stage requirements, and then assign tasks to everyone.

13. Practice writing more characters.

笔画数						

Additional Vocabulary

参加	cānjiā	to attend; to join
滑冰	huábīng	to skate
滑雪	huáxuě	to ski
划艇	huátǐng	rowboat
跆拳道	táiquándào	taekwondo
舞蹈	wǔdǎo	dance
读书	dú shū	to read

第二十二课 我们一到假期就去旅行

1. Write the tones of the words or phrases, then translate them.

xia xue	likai	shoupiaochu	laihuipiao	yiwai	huaxue
下雪	离开	售票处	来回票	意外	滑雪
jiaqi	lüxing	danchengpiao	lüxingshe	daoda	liubing
假期	旅行	单程票	旅行社	到达	溜冰

2. Write the characters.

笔画数						
	jià					
	lí					
	lǚ					

	dān					
	chéng					
	yīng					

3. Make new words or phrases based on the characters given.

开 kāi	到 dào	行 xíng	外 wài	气 qì	期 qī	报 bào
雪 xuě	票 piào	售 shòu	备 bèi	准 zhǔn	天 tiān	单 dān
旅 lǚ	订 dìng	达 dá	假 jià	离 lí	下 xià	意 yì
处 chù	预 yù	程 chéng	要 yào	票 piào	是 shì	票 piào

1) ____________ 2) ____________ 3) ____________

4) ____________ 5) ____________ 6) ____________

7) ____________ 8) ____________ 9) ____________

10) ____________ 11) ____________ 12) ____________ 13) ____________

4. Write characters using the following radicals.

扌 ______________________________

讠 ______________________________

5. Fill in the blanks with the given words following the text.

坐　旅行　订

1) 今年冬天我和家人去加拿大______。我去旅行社______了来回票，要是没有意外的天气，我们就星期六______飞机去加拿大。

一　可是　就　虽然

2) 这个星期六我和家人去加拿大旅行。______冬天常常下雪，______没关系，我喜欢下雪。天气预报说星期六天气很好，我很高兴。我______到加拿大，______给你打电话，好吗?

6. Complete the sentences following the examples.

1)

他	一	喝酒	就	喝醉	。
我		爬山		累	。
					。

2)

老师	一	问问题	，	同学们	就	回答	。
小明		发烧	，	妈妈	就	给他吃药	。
							。

3)

你	什么时候	上课	?
学校		考试	?
			?

7. Make sentences to describe the pictures by rearranging the words.

1) 就　他　高兴　唱歌　一

____

2) 哥哥 一 电话 饭馆 外卖 就 给 打 送 他

____

3) 你　有　什么　星期三　时候　比赛

____

4) 不　要是　出去　下雪　我们　就

____

8. Decide True (T) or False (F) according to Exercise 4 of the Student's Book.

1) 老师问哥哥很多问题。(　　)
2) 下雪的时候树木和房子都很漂亮。(　　)
3) "我"买了来回票，星期六晚上可以回家。(　　)
4) "我们"常常去非洲旅行,"我"很喜欢非洲的森林和动物。(　　)

9. What is your favourite mode of transportation when traveling? Why?

____

____

____

10. Fill in the blanks with the correct characters and write a similar paragraph of your own.

我和哥哥都______中学学习，我们都很喜欢旅行。______到假期我们______去旅行，我们去______很多地方，也有很多照片（zhàopiàn, photo）。我们常常______朋友们一起看照片，说旅行的事，很有意思。这是去年我们______雪和______冰的照片，你知道哪个人是我吗？

____

____

____

11. Listen and answer the following questions.

1) "我"在哪儿学习？

____

2) "我"假期想去哪儿？为什么？

____

3) 去那个地方的票贵吗？

____

4) "我"每个假期都去那儿吗？"我"跟谁一起去？

____

12. Tell your partner a story about your travels. Talk about the preparation for the trip, how the journey was, and give him or her some advice about traveling.

13. Practice writing more characters.

笔画数

Additional Vocabulary

照片	zhàopiàn	photo
旅行包	lǚxíngbāo	traveling bag
导游	dǎoyóu	guide
租	zū	to rent

第二十三课　我要从美国到中国去

1. Write the tones of the words or phrases, then translate them.

xingli	lüguan	xiaoshi	hai	lüxingdai
行李	旅馆	小时	海	旅行袋
huzhao	tingliu	canguan	yinhang	dianzi youjian
护照	停留	参观	银行	电子邮件

2. Write the characters.

笔画数						
	hù					
	zhào					
	yín					

	zhī					
	tíng					
	liú					

3. Make new words or phrases based on the characters given.

照 zhào	纪 jì	护 hù	行 xíng	旅 lǚ	行 háng
时 shí	支 zhī	景 jǐng	银 yín	念 niàn	留 liú
停 tíng	行 xíng	馆 guǎn	风 fēng	李 lǐ	票 piào
品 pǐn	海 hǎi	小 xiǎo	旅 lǚ	滩 tān	袋 dài

1) ____________ 2) ____________ 3) ____________

4) ____________ 5) ____________ 6) ____________

7) __________ 8) __________ 9) __________ 10) __________

4. Write characters using the following radicals.

氵 ________________________________

纟 ________________________________

5. Fill in the blanks with the given words following the text.

准备　停留　到

1) 明天我要______中国去，在北京______一个星期。还要到新加坡去，在新加坡停留三天。我______了护照和旅行支票，还买了一个旅行袋。

电话　地方　电子邮件　纪念品

2) 假期我们班很多同学都要去旅行，我去欧洲，丽丽去日本，小红去泰国，小海去马来西亚。我们可以看很多______，还可以买______。我们互相（hùxiāng, each other）打______，也互相写______。

6. Complete the sentences following the examples.

1)

我	要	从	美国	到	中国	去	。
			机场		市中心		。
							。

2)

从	伦敦	到	纽约	坐飞机去	要	几个小时	？
	家		购物中心	坐地铁去			？
							？

3)

从	家	到	学校	坐公共汽车去	要	一个小时	。
	博物馆		动物园				。
							。

7. Make sentences to describe the pictures by rearranging the words.

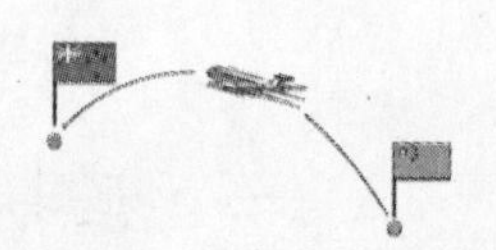

1) 我 中国 新西兰 去 要 到 从

____

2) 火车站 旅馆 地铁 小时 半 从 到 个 去 坐 要

____

3) 四 我 在 个 要 停留 小时 纽约

____

4) 不 旅馆 银行 远 离

____

8. Decide True (T) or False (F) according to Exercise 4 of the Student's Book.

1) 火车票售票处的人不多。(　　)
2) 从“我”家到广州坐飞机去快。(　　)
3) “我”今年暑假不离开北京。(　　)
4) 从学校到火车站坐公共汽车去很快。(　　)

9. Which countries have you been to? How did you get there? How long does it take to get there?

____

____

____

10. Fill in the blanks with the correct characters and write a similar paragraph of your own.

我家在欧洲，在欧洲旅行很方便（fāngbiàn, convenient），坐汽车、火车和飞机______可以，可是有的时候坐火车______坐飞机贵。很多国家______我的城市不远，假期我常常跟爸爸妈妈去很多地方参观。

____

____

____

11. Listen and answer the following questions.

1) “我”家在哪儿？

____

2) “我”想去哪儿旅行？

____

3) 今年暑假“我”去哪儿旅行？坐什么去？要多少个小时？

____

4) “我”喜欢坐火车吗？为什么？

____

12. Discuss a travel plan with your partner. Talk about what destination you want to go to, how you will get there, where you will stay, what you want to experience, and what you need to take with you.

13. Practice writing more characters.

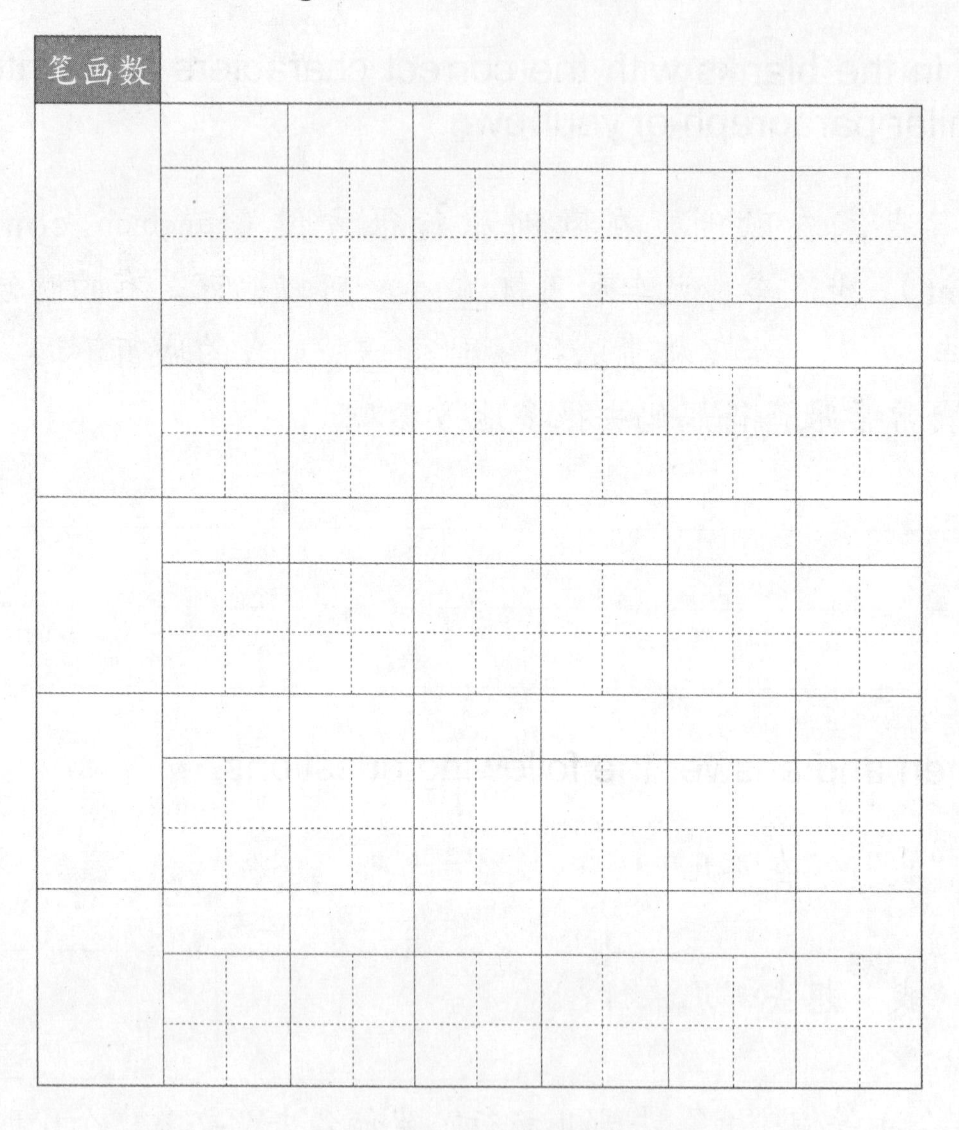

Additional Vocabulary

分钟	fēnzhōng	minute
自然	zìrán	nature

第二十四课　在中国过年

1. Write the tones of the words or phrases, then translate them.

guonian	kuaile	qiwen	Shengdan Jie	na	duoyun
过年	快乐	气温	圣诞节	拿	多云
fuwutai	wu shi	wu long	Chunjie	deng	zhu
服务台	舞狮	舞龙	春节	等	祝

2. Write the characters.

笔画数						
	jiā					
	wù					
	ná					

	bǎ					
	wēn					
	yà					

3. Make new words or phrases based on the characters given.

龙 lóng	服 fú	气 qì	春 chūn	舞 wǔ	节 jié	风 fēng
物 wù	欢 huān	俗 sú	员 yuán	年 nián	舞 wǔ	快 kuài
新 xīn	节 jié	狮 shī	年 nián	乐 lè	迎 yíng	子 zi
过 guò	温 wēn	礼 lǐ	饺 jiǎo	多 duō	务 wù	云 yún

1) ________ 2) ________ 3) ________

4) ________ 5) ________ 6) ________

7) ________ 8) ________ 9) ________

10) ________ 11) ________ 12) ________

4. Write characters using the following radicals.

忄 ________________________

冫 ________________________

5. Fill in the blanks with the given words following the text.

等 坐 去

1) 今年我要______明明家过年，我很高兴。明明家在北京，我______飞机去。明明和他的爸爸妈妈在家______我，他们给我准备了新年礼物。

给 到 拿

2) 今天天气不好，我很晚才______明明的家。我到的时候，他和爸爸妈妈正等我呢。妈妈把菜______来，我把我妈妈的礼物______他们。

6. Complete the sentences following the examples.

1)

他	是	坐	公共汽车	来	学校	的	。
		开	车		机场		。
							。

2)

他们	正	看电视	呢	。
		表演		。
				。

3)

服务员	把	菜单	拿	来	了	。
		飞机票	买			。
						。

7. Make sentences to describe the pictures by rearranging the words.

1) 地铁 他 来 坐 是 的

____

2) 学生们 足球 比赛 正 呢 进行

____

3) 妈妈 拿来 把 咖啡 了

____

4) 上海 北京 没有 冷

____

8. Answer the following questions according to Exercise 4 of the Student's Book.

1) Mike今年在哪儿过年？他高兴吗？

____

2) “我”怎么来北京？为什么来？

____

3) “我”的身体怎么样？为什么？

____

4) “我”和朋友一起去哪儿？

____

9. Tell your partner how you spent the Christmas holidays last year.

____

____

____

10. What do you know about China's Spring Festival? Bring some decorations for the Spring Festival or learn to exchange holiday greetings in Chinese.

____

____

____

11. Fill in the blanks with the correct characters and write a similar paragraph of your own.

春节是我最喜欢的中国节日（jiéri, festival），春节的时候爸爸妈妈都不工作，准备很多好吃的______。孩子们最高兴，晚上他们可以不______，吃饺子，放鞭炮（biānpào, fireworks），还可以拿到红包（hóngbāo, pocket money in red envelopes）。新年的时候还可以看很多表演。每个人都说："祝你______快乐！"

____

____

____

____

12. Listen and answer the following questions.

1) “我”是哪国人？在哪儿学习？

____

2) “我”常常回中国吗？

____

3) 今年春节“我”去了哪儿？

____

4) “我”春节的时候做了什么？

____

13. Write and perform a play for your classmates about the Spring Festival. Use the following scenes as a guide:

- Several thousands of years ago, people would make fires and loud noises to scare away demons.
- Then people began to welcome the coming new year with a week of celebrations. They would pray to family gods, clean the house, and put up lanterns, New Year decorations, door-gods, and *Fu* characters. They would make tofu and *mantou,* and buy meat and wine.
- Nowadays, people celebrate the new year on New Year's Eve. Families gather, have dinner, watch television, make dumplings to eat at midnight, and wish each a "Happy New Year!" Older members of the family also give *hongbao*, pocket money in red envelopes, to the young ones.

14. Practice writing more characters.

笔画数

Additional Vocabulary

放假	fàngjià	to take a holiday
恭喜发财	gōngxǐ fācái	may you be prosperous

附录：1. 录音文本*

第一课

1）你好，我叫Mike，今年十五岁，我是美国人。

2）今年暑假我去了中国的北京，看了有名的故宫和长城，故宫和长城真漂亮。

3）我有很多新朋友，他们都是北京的学生，有男孩子，也有女孩子。

4）我们一起说英语，真有意思。我不会说汉语，我很想跟他们一起说汉语，所以我想学汉语。

第二课

1）我去过很多地方，除了英国以外，我还去过德国和美国。

2）虽然每个地方都很好，可是美国的海滩最漂亮，风景好极了。

3）我跟爸爸、妈妈一起游泳，还在海滩上踢足球。

4）暑假快要来了，今年夏天我跟爸爸妈妈去中国，我太高兴了。

第三课

1）Mary今天感冒了，她没有来上课，我晚上给她打了电话。

2）虽然她很不舒服，可是她现在越来越好了。

3）她去了医院，医生说，每天喝很多水，休息休息，可以好一点儿。

4）我明天去她家看看，我给她准备了新买的唱片。

第四课

1）春天的时候有端午节，我看龙舟，吃粽子。

2）秋天的时候有中秋节，我吃月饼。

3）夏天的时候我去海滩，中国的东边和南边有很多海滩，漂亮极了。

4）我出生的城市有八十多个学校，每个学校都有汉语课。

5）香港没有北京那么冷，北京的冬天冷得不得了。

---

* 本文本的录音文件附在学生用书录音文件后。

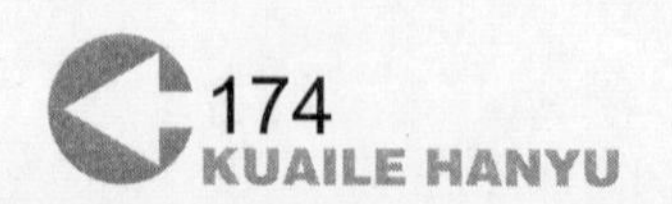

第五课

1）去年我去了长城，长城在北京的北边，离市中心很远。

2）爸爸会开汽车，我不会，我每天坐公共汽车去学校。

3）花园里除了有红花，也有白色的花，绿色的草也很漂亮。

4）您是司机吧？我要去北京火车站，离天安门广场不远。

第六课

1）我家在公路旁边，离汽车站很近，公路上有很多汽车。

2）我喜欢学习地理，喜欢看地图，地图里有街道、铁路和公路。

3）我家离体育馆和图书馆都不很远，星期六上午我去图书馆看书，下午去体育馆打网球。

4）这个城市虽然很小，可是街道和商店都很干净，花和树木都很漂亮。

第七课

1）我跟我父母一起在郊区，我家的房子不很大，可是很舒服。

2）我家有客厅、厨房、两个卧室、两个浴室，客厅和卧室里有地毯，冰箱在厨房里。

3）我家旁边有一个超市，还有一个图书馆，我们常常到超市去买东西，到图书馆去看书。

4）我很喜欢我的家，我的朋友常常来我家，也欢迎你到我家来。

第八课

1）明天是妈妈的生日，我和姐姐想送她一个礼物。我问姐姐送什么好，她也不怎么清楚。

2）我和姐姐一起去了百货商场，因为这个百货商场比那个购物中心更好，有很多可爱的东西。

3）妈妈很喜欢中国音乐，所以我们给她买了一张中国唱片，好听极了。

4）姐姐买了一个照相机，因为她要去中国。我买了一条裙子，跟广告里的一样。

第九课

1）今年冬天我去了中国。中国的风景很漂亮，人也很好。我去了很多地方，还买了很多纪念品。

2）在中国，我有一个新朋友，他请我去他家，还请我看京剧，有意思极了。我很喜欢他。

3）他的妻子是老师，儿子在百货商场工作，孙子是小学生，他们都会说英语。

4）朋友送了我很多礼物，除了国画，还有唱片。现在我常常给他们打电话，我想请他们来英国。

第十课

我是小海的朋友Mike，我在北京学习汉语。我的老师是中国人，他常常问问题，我喜欢回答问题。我说汉语说得不太好，我的中国同学常常跟我一起说汉语、做汉语练习，他们回答我的问题回答得很清楚，现在我的汉语越来越好。

第十一课

我叫小海，我在北京的中学学习，我很喜欢我的学校，我们在学校里除了上课，还有很多活动。我是学校的乒乓球队的。每天下午要是天气好，我们就在运动场训练，要是天气不好，我们就在体育馆训练。我的同学丽丽是戏剧队的。他们常常在礼堂练习表演。我看过他们表演的中国戏剧，他们表演得好极了，这个星期天他们要表演英国戏剧，我和同学都要去看。

第十二课

我的爸爸在大学工作，他是大学的老师。他喜欢上网看新闻，我也喜欢看网上的新闻。除了看新闻，我还喜欢听网上的音乐。我的笔友跟我一样喜欢听音乐。我的妹妹喜欢电脑游戏，她的爱好跟我不一样。

第十三课

我不常生病，因为我喜欢运动。爷爷每天去公园打太极拳，他的耳朵不好。妹妹常常胃疼，她每天都吃药，她喜欢吃中药。要是妈妈头疼，她就吃西药。

第十四课

我们一家都喜欢运动，奶奶每天去公园散步，妈妈去体育馆游泳，爸爸星期天骑两个钟头的马，我跟哥哥星期六下午踢一个钟头的足球。哥哥和我是学生，我们每天写半个钟头的作业。

第十五课

我们家的晚饭很好吃，我们吃米饭，也吃面条儿。晚饭后，爸爸喜欢喝一点儿葡萄酒。妈妈常常喝茶。她喝红茶，也喝绿茶。我和哥哥喜欢吃冰激凌。

第十六课

1）我们城市的动物园里有两只熊猫，熊猫从中国来，很可爱。
2）我喜欢跟老年人一起看京剧，看京剧的时候，他们高兴极了，我也很高兴。
3）听音乐会的时候，Mike买了很多中国音乐的CD，他要送朋友礼物。
4）我从来没见过熊猫，我去动物园的时候，熊猫生病了。

第十七课

1）图书馆每天早上九点开，我八点半从我家去图书馆，我家离图书馆不远。
2）我和我的朋友都喜欢上网，下课以后，谁都不回家，我们去图书馆看网上的新闻。
3）中国国家博物馆外面的风景很好，有天安门广场，有故宫，漂亮极了。
4）要是你喜欢看书，就来我们学校的图书馆吧，图书馆里有很多书。

5）中国国家图书馆是中国最大的图书馆，每天有很多人来看书，图书馆的书多极了。

第十八课

1）爬山的时候天气不好，没有太阳。

2）我们从山下边跑上去，每个人都跑得很快，我们比赛爬山。

3）我口渴了，也饿了，我们在森林里吃饭吧!

4）刮风了，天空有很多云，快要下雨了。

5）城市的西边有很多山，北边也有很多山，西边的山和北边的山一样高。

第十九课

1）你有没有看今天网上的新闻？新闻说，我们的地球污染问题越来越大，我们这个城市的污染问题也很大。

2）网上的新闻很多，有欧洲的、美洲的、非洲的、亚洲的，要是你想看，什么都有。

3）今天我在网上看到了一个印度风俗展览，有意思极了，谁都很喜欢。你有没有上网看看？

第二十课

1）李先生是本地新闻的记者，每天在城市里采访。他采访医生、工人、售货员，也采访演员、画家和名人。

2）因为他的零用钱不太多，所以星期二和星期天在一个饭馆兼职，一天工作五个钟头。你看，现在他正在工作。

3）今天是哥哥的生日，我和父母给他买了生日礼物，一个摄像机和一个录音笔。我们回家的时候，他正在看电视，看到了礼物，他高兴地跑过来。

4）我跟朋友一起去市中心，我们都买了很多东西，花了很多钱。我们去饭馆的时候，爸爸正在那个饭馆吃饭，他替我们付了账单。

第二十一课

1）我是一个中学生，我的爱好很多，除了爱好运动和上网，我还喜欢汉语。我是学校中文俱乐部的会员。

2）现在我们俱乐部正在教中文歌，因为学校每年有一个用中文唱歌的比赛，我们请马老师教我们，她唱歌唱得好极了。

3）我还是俱乐部中文报纸的记者，常常在学校里采访老师和学生，我们的网页上有我写的新闻，你有没有看过？

4）明年我就毕业了，我想暑假到中国去。为什么？因为我要去看看我的笔友，现在我们常常用中文写电子邮件，他是我的好朋友。

第二十二课

我在英国的中学学习，我快要毕业了。我想一到假期就去伦敦。我想去博物馆看看。伦敦的博物馆很多，也很有意思，去伦敦的来回票不贵。我每个假期都跟朋友一起去伦敦。

第二十三课

我家在中国的西边，我很想去中国的南边旅行。我今年暑假到广州去旅行。从我住的城市到广州坐火车要二十个小时，坐飞机要三个小时。我买了火车票。我昨天离开家，在火车上看窗外，风景漂亮极了，我很高兴。

第二十四课

我是中国人，在英国的大学学习，每个假期我都回北京。虽然今年北京的冬天很冷，可是我春节去了很多地方。我去了爷爷奶奶家，祝他们新年快乐。他们给我很多新年礼物。我还跟他们一起看了舞狮和舞龙。

2. 部分参考答案

第一课　我从北京来

5. 1）十五　五　电视　音乐　运动　有名　2）丽丽　小红　上海　香港

7. 1）我从北京来。
   2）我家在上海。
   3）我想去很多国家。
   4）欢迎你来长城。

第二课　我想来兼职

5. 1）休息　电脑　上课　运动　2）想　会　能

7. 1）除了游泳以外，我还喜欢足球。
   2）卧室虽然小，可是很舒服。
   3）她打得不很好。/她打得很不好。
   4）他在运动场表演过太极拳。
   5）他想来学习书法。

第三课　我们给他打电话吧

5. 1）来　说　做　工作　试试　2）饿　吃　打　送　点

7. 1）那个教室是我们的。
   2）妈妈替妹妹穿衣服。
   3）老师给学生上课。
   4）我的肚子很饿。
   5）我有那个学校的电话。

第四课　北京有一个很大的广场

5. 1）市中心　东边　北边　2）很　没有　那么　过

7. 1）市中心有一个很大的花园。

   2）米饭没有面条好吃。

   3）我有三十多个朋友。

   4）汉语考试很难。

   5）汽车站在商店的北边。

第五课　郊区没有污染

5. 1）离　开　坐　2）远　近　除了　还

7. 1）我家旁边有很多的树木。

   2）房间里的空气不好。

   3）商店离汽车站不远。

   4）夏天热得不得了。

   5）我现在饿极了。

第六课　我是本地人

5. 1）本地　铁路　公路　土地　2）警察局　厕所

7. 1）我家离警察局很近。

   2）卧室和客厅都不很大。

   3）她在花园里找小猫。

   4）这个地区的学校很多。

   5）这个城市的街道都很干净。

第七课　我的新家

5. 1）从　来　住　爸爸　2）浴室　层　舒服　到

   3）超市　看看　什么　以前

7. 1）下午我们要到运动场去踢足球。

   2）欢迎你们到我的新家来。

3）爸爸给我买了书桌和书架。

4）王先生是张明的朋友，他从上海来。

第八课　我想送她一个礼物

5. 1）生日　先　还　送　礼物　　2）照相机　孙女　裙子　漂亮

7. 1）这个冰箱是德国的吧？

2）百货商场和购物中心都不怎么远。

3）我姐姐的房间比我的更干净。

4）马太太给孙女买了一条白裙子。

5）他问我百货商场在哪儿。

第九课　他买到了纪念品

5. 1）商场　英国　国画　中文　一些　　2）买到了　买不到　买得到　离

7. 1）王先生买到了最喜欢的国画。

2）他没买到飞机票，所以他坐火车去。

3）姐姐请我跟她一起去看电影。

4）在这个商场买得到纪念品，可是买不到水果。

5）书店离这个公园不远，一直走。

第十课　你说汉语说得真好

5. 1）毕业　考试　上　写　做　　2）中学　得　说　问题　　3）去　难　坐

7. 1）他的老师打篮球打得很好。

2）这个汉字很难写，那个汉字不难写。

3）他回答问题回答得很清楚。

4）课本上的这个练习不难做。

第十一课　比赛四点才开始

5. 1）星期天　在　队　队员　要是　　2）开始　才　没有　看看

7. 1）体操队三点半才开始训练。

2）电影八点才开始，现在去吃饭吧。

3）我们喜欢戏剧，你要是不去就听音乐会。

4）星期天学校要是没有活动，我们就去海滩。

第十二课　看看我的电子邮件

5. 1）小学　上　新闻　信　笔友　　2）看看　电子　有　都　成年

7. 1）妈妈跟爸爸一样喜欢中国京剧。

2）现在七点，我们看看新闻吧。

3）我要是有困难，同学就帮助我。

4）爸爸今天在网上买了电影票。

5）我的中文写对了，可是英文写错了。

第十三课　他从来没吃过中药

5. 1）病　学校　疼　医院　西药　中药

2）伤风　头　休息　吃　喝　好　可能

7. 1）我从来没坐过飞机。

2）哥哥和我昨天都病了。

3）小红喉咙疼得很。

4）伤风了应该多喝水。

5）你要是明天好了就去上课。/明天你要是好了，就去上课。

第十四课　我的身体越来越好

5. 1）老少　公园　湖边　骑马　家务　钟头　健康

2）喜欢　胖　要是　就　常常　打　有用

7. 1）她每天做几个钟头的运动。

2）你喜不喜欢运动?

3）爸爸每天七点半就去工作。

4）要是常常打篮球，就越来越高了。

5）我不踢足球，因为我太瘦了。

6）运动对健康很有用。

7）这个孩子差不多六岁了。

第十五课　我们都爱吃她做的点心

5. 1）吃饭　早饭　喝　煮　中午　晚饭　炒

2）爱　饭　也　好吃　很久　喝酒　喝醉

7. 1）你吃过中国菜没有？

2）我打篮球，也踢足球。

3）哥哥做的早饭不好吃。

4）老师写的汉字很好看。

5）我们都爱吃意大利人做的面条儿。

6）哥哥很久没有上网了。

第十六课　熊猫可爱极了

5. 1）只　去　看　极　　2）过来　站　高兴

3）市场　跟　一样　　4）坏了　新的　一起

7. 1）孩子们可爱极了！

2）我和朋友去市场买明信片了。

3）我们去的时候，熊猫已经开始吃饭了。

4）孩子们都站起来了。

5）小狗高兴地跑过来。

6）我去商店买新眼镜。

第十七课　我们都在图书馆看书

5. 1）常常　阅读　科技　　2）以后　都　在

3）外边　里　旁边　　4）开　关　转

7. 1）我们都在运动场踢足球。

2）小明常常阅读地理书。

3）博物馆外面有一个大花园。

4）我们学校离湖边很近。

5）我家窗外有一个大广告。

6）从车站过去就能看见出口。

第十八课 我们都跑上山去

5. 1）爬山 天气 太阳 2）从 上 快 3）北边 森林 一样

7. 1）我们都跑上山去。

2）爷爷和奶奶从山上边走下来。

3）天空有很多云，快要下雨了。

4）图书馆的地理书和历史书一样多。

5）火车站在电影院和博物馆中间。

第十九课 有什么新闻

5. 1）多 访问 高 大 比赛 2）展览 艺术 开始 知道

7. 1）他现在有没有睡觉？/现在他有没有睡觉？

2）你有没有给他打过电话？

3）我什么问题都没有。

4）他什么博物馆都去过。

5）他的身体越来越瘦。

第二十课 他正在采访

5. 1）网页 记者 采访 花 2）赚 给 付

7. 1）爷爷正在打太极拳。

2）我去看他的时候，他正在发烧。

3）我请她帮助同学。

4）我问他谁有照相机。

5）这个问题怎么回答？

第二十一课 中文歌表演比赛

5. 1）名人 记者 新闻 2）用 请 教 比

7. 1）我用信用卡付账。

2）我开车开得比他快。/他开车开得比我快。

3）我请王先生访问我们学校。

4）他是网球俱乐部的会员。

5）我今天买的CD很好听。/今天我买的CD很好听。

第二十二课　我们一到假期就去旅行

5. 1）旅行　订　坐　　2）虽然　可是　一　就

7. 1）他一高兴就唱歌。

2）哥哥一打电话，饭馆就给他送外卖。

3）星期三你什么时候有比赛？/你星期三什么时候有比赛？

4）要是不下雪我们就出去。/要是下雪我们就不出去。

第二十三课　我要从美国到中国去

5. 1）到　停留　准备　　2）地方　纪念品　电话　电子邮件

7. 1）我要从中国到新西兰去。

2）从火车站坐地铁到旅馆去要半个小时。

3）我要在纽约停留四个小时。

4）银行离旅馆不远。

第二十四课　在中国过年

5. 1）去　坐　等　　2）到　拿　给

7. 1）他是坐地铁来的。

2）学生们正进行足球比赛呢！

3）妈妈把咖啡拿来了。

4）上海没有北京冷。

KUAILE HANYU

快乐汉语

练习册

（英语版）

主编　李晓琪

编者　宣　雅　刘晓雨　王淑红

人民教育出版社

·北京·

总　策　划　许　琳　殷忠民　韦志榕
总　监　制　夏建辉　郑旺全
监　　　制　张彤辉　刘根芹
　　　　　　王世友　赵晓非

编　　　者　李晓琪　罗青松　刘晓雨
　　　　　　王淑红　宣　雅

责任编辑　李　津
审　　　稿　狄国伟　王世友
英文审稿　Miriam Ruth Fisher［美］

美术编辑　张　蓓
封面设计　金　葆
插图制作　李思东工作室

图书在版编目（CIP）数据

快乐汉语（第二版）练习册：英语版. 第3册 / 李晓琪等编. —北京：人民教育出版社，2015.7

ISBN 978-7-107-23191-9

Ⅰ. ①快… Ⅱ. ①李… Ⅲ. ①汉语—对外汉语教学—习题集 Ⅳ. ①H195.4

中国版本图书馆CIP数据核字（2015）第158540号

人民教育出版社 出版发行
网址：http://www.pep.com.cn
大厂益利印刷有限公司印装　全国新华书店经销
2015年7月第1版　2015年8月第1次印刷
开本：890毫米×1 240毫米　1/16　印张：12
字数：220千字　印数：0 001～3 000册
定价：71.00元